MASTERCRAFT

2. HEALTH, HYGIENE AND SAFETY IN THE HOTEL AND CATERING INDUSTRY

Marion Kenber

and William McCurrach
Glasgow College of Food Technology

Series Editor: Roy Hayter, Hotel and Catering Training Company

MACMILLAN

First published 1990

Published by
MACMILLAN EDUCATION LTD
Houndmills, Basingstoke, Hampshire RG21 2XS
and London
Companies and representatives
throughout the world

Printed in Great Britain by
Scotprint Ltd, Musselburgh

British Library Cataloguing in Publication Data
Kenber, Marion
    Health, hygiene and safety in the hotel and catering
    industry.—(MASTERCRAFT; 2).
    1. Great Britain. Hotel & catering industries.
    Industrial health & industrial safety
    I. Title   II. McCurrach, William III. Series
    363.1′1964794′0941

ISBN 0–333–45789–7

CONTENTS

CONTENTS

Fire

Security

Health, hygiene and safety

CONTENTS

ACKNOWLEDGEMENTS

Macmillan Education and the Hotel and Catering Training Company are grateful to Mary James and Melvyn Teare who were responsible for setting up the original structure and scope of this book, to Gillian Wright who commented on the draft text, to Jennifer Kimber who helped edit the text, to Jennifer Murray who also helped edit the text and who briefed and organised the photographic sessions with Catherine Blackie.

The publishers would also like to express sincere thanks to the following for their help in supplying photographs and illustrations:

Allibert Leisure Furniture, Cowes (units 31 and 49)

Beefeater Steak House, Surbiton (units 6, 16, 37 and 44)

Catherine Blackie (picture research, photographs in units 3 and 20, and at Beefeater Steak House, Flemings Hotel, Granada Motorway Services, Inn on the Park and Princess Louise)

Burford Bridge Hotel (Trusthouse Forte), Box Hill, Dorking (cover, photographer Transmedia)

W M Christy & Co (unit 26)

Copthorne Hotels (unit 46, The Copthorne, Plymouth and unit 48, The Copthorne, Birmingham)

Crest Hotels Ltd (units 3 and 15)

The Electricity Council, London (line illustrations in units 36 and 42)

Evening Argus, Brighton (unit 2)

Flemings Hotel, Mayfair, London (units 4, 5, 7, 14, 20, 24, 27, 29, 32, 43, 45 and 46)

Fire Protection Association (unit 19, photographer Douglas C. Morris & Co.)

Fire Protection Services, Birmingham (unit 21)

Format Photographers Ltd (units 10 and 31, photographer Jenny Matthews; unit 12, photographer Michael Ann Mullen; unit 30, photographer Maggie Murray; units 9, 11 and 28, photographer Brenda Prince and unit 32, photographer Joanne O'Brien)

The Fresh Fruit and Vegetable Information Bureau, London (unit 9)

Gardner Merchant Ltd, Manchester (unit 37)

Granada Motorway Services Ltd, Heston Services M4 (units 25, 42, and 43)

Sally and Richard Greenhill, Photographers Photo Library (units 7, 10, 11, 14 and 24)

Guidepost Hotel, Bradford (unit 40, photographer Robin Matthams)

The Inn on the Park, London (units 15, 19, 28, 38, 39, 40 and 47)

Little Chef (units 6 and 12)

London Tara Hotel (unit 17, photographer Catherine Blackie, units 3, 6, 23, 29, 32, 33 and 36, photographer Alexia Cross)

Novotel, Hammersmith, London (unit 12, photographer Picture Link)

The Press Association Ltd, London (unit 18)

The Princess Louise, Holborn, London (units 22, 23, 28, 32 and 41)

Rentokil Environmental Services Division (units 34 and 35)

Rex Features Ltd (units 1, 2 and 20)

The Royal Marsden Hospital (units 28 and 32, photographer Alexia Cross)

The Savoy Hotel, Strand, London (unit 3)

Science Photo Library (unit 35, photographer Dr Tony Brain)

Rob Shone, London (line illustrations in units 5, 12, 14, 18, 21, 29, 30 and 37)

David Spears Ltd, Stevenage (units 38 and 39)

St John Ambulance, St Andrew's Ambulance Association and The British Red

ACKNOWLEDGEMENTS

Cross Society (for permission to adapt the illustrations in units 51, 52, 54, 55, 56, 59 and 60 from *First Aid Manual*, Dorling Kindersley Ltd, London, 1988). The text in units 50 to 60 is also based on the same source
Stocksigns Ltd, Redhill (unit 15)
Thistle Hotels Ltd (unit 26, The Lowndes Thistle)
Thorn Security Ltd, Oldham (unit 21)

Publisher's note

While every effort has been made to ensure that the information is correct, *Health, Hygiene and Safety in the Hotel and Catering Industry* should not be regarded as a complete or authoritative statement of the law. Readers are urged to seek appropriate guidance when they are in any doubt, and will need to note changes in legislation after June 1989.

More than 4000 accidents to customers and staff in the hotel and catering industry are reported every year in the UK. In particular, the number of cases of food poisoning rose sharply during the 1980s and continues to increase.

Health, hygiene and safety is a part of almost every task, whether it is preparing or serving food, keeping the premises clean, or simply moving from one task to the next. Everyone, not just the management, but the staff as well, has a responsibility to do all they can to protect themselves, the people they work with, and their customers.

The structure of the book

The book is divided into 60 self-contained units, grouped into nine major subject areas.

The customer—this unit looks at the customer's viewpoint, for without customers there would be no hotel and catering jobs.

Insight—these two units explore the main issues of safety and hygiene in the hotel and catering industry.

The impression you give—how everyone working in hotels, catering, leisure and tourism can make a positive contribution to their workplace, their customers and their colleagues.

Your health—keeping healthy and fit.

The law—a comprehensive summary of the legislation on health, safety and hygiene.

Fire—what causes fires, how they can be prevented, fire fighting techniques and evacuation procedures.

Security—procedures which will help protect the workplace, the property and well-being of customers, staff and owners.

Health, hygiene and safety—the major section of this book. The first nine units cover the aspects that are relevant to all hotel and catering work. A further 13 units deal with specific work areas including food preparation, food service, barwork, housekeeping, front of house, stores and leisure.

First aid—an introduction to first aid procedures designed to encourage and support practical training under the supervision of a qualified first aider.

Each unit has a TO DO, an activity designed to encourage interest, to help the reader apply the information to his or her own experience and to develop a deeper understanding of the subject.

The information in this book will help the reader gain the following Caterbase introductory modules:

- *Personal Presentation and Personal Hygiene*
  units 4 to 11
- *Safe Working*
  units 2, 12 to 15, 18 to 22 and 28 to 49
- *Hygiene Practices*
  units 3, 4, 16, 17 and 31 to 49
- *Efficient Working*
  units 7, 37 to 49 (see also *Mastercraft 1: Working in the Hotel and Catering Industry*)
- *Emergency Aid at Work*
  units 50 to 60.

1 THE CUSTOMER

Most people spend some time away from home through choice, or because they have to. They may be away on holiday, staying at a hotel or caravan site. They may be on a day trip to enjoy the sights of London, Cardiff or Edinburgh. They may be away on business or studying at college. They may have been sentenced to prison. Or they may be ill in hospital.

Establishments customers use

Some premises such as hotels and hospitals are usually residential; in other words they provide overnight accommodation. Others like restaurants and pubs are generally non-residential. Many establishments are privately owned and run on a profit-making basis, such as hotels and leisure centres. Schools and office or factory cafeterias are usually subsidised by the local authority or the employer, and are considered non-profit making. National Health Service hospitals and local authority residential homes for children, and elderly or disabled people, are also non-profit making institutions. There are also hospitals and residential homes for the elderly which are privately owned and profit making.

What customers want

The expectations of customers will usually vary according to the type of establishment they are visiting and the price they are paying. For instance, customers eating lunch or dinner in the restaurant of a motorway service station will know they cannot buy alcohol to drink with their meal, nor would they order a sirloin steak at a vegetarian restaurant. But whatever the circumstances, regardless of how much they are paying, all customers — holiday makers, people on business, patients, hotel guests, sportsmen and women, and travellers alike — have the right to demand that the establishments they use are safe, secure and hygienic. After all, in the hotel, catering, leisure and tourism industry, vast numbers of customers and staff are involved—at any one time each building might contain many persons and their property, and any customers who feel they and their possessions are at risk will not wish to use that establishment.

How to give customers what they want

There is little point in offering excellent facilities and service if safety and hygiene have been neglected. An olympic-size swimming pool is of no use to the swimmer if the water filter system is not properly maintained. Flowers and complimentary champagne will not impress the honeymoon couple one bit if the bathroom of their suite looks as if it has not been cleaned thoroughly.

So staff need to have not only good personal skills and a knowledge of what facilities their establishment can offer, but also an understanding of why it is so important that they do their job in a safe and hygienic manner, and how they can accomplish this.

Other reasons people stay away from home are:

travelling
meeting friends/family
weddings or funerals
sporting/leisure activity
military duty
attending conferences
celebrating a special event
visiting a person in hospital
having a baby
being cared for if homeless or disabled

Establishments include:

hotels	hospitals
guesthouses	trains and planes
leisure centres	boats and ferries
restaurants, cafés	residential homes
halls of residence	conference centres
prisons	theme parks
caravan parks	holiday camps
take-aways	pubs
wine bars	clubs
cocktail bars	bistros
cafeterias	stately homes
theatres	cinemas
brasseries	boarding schools
approved schools	youth hostels
museums	art galleries

Tell-tale signs

Customers quickly pick up the atmosphere in a place, and if anything is wrong it will soon be discovered. The following signs are a sure indication that standards of safety and hygiene are suspect, even though this may not be so!

harassed staff
chipped china or glassware
dirty bathrooms/toilets
tables not cleared
rooms not serviced properly
stained linen
untidy public areas
poor service
noisy behind the scenes
untidy, unclean staff
poor security
accident and fire hazards

If people are in the position of choosing where to spend their time, it is often because they wish to enjoy themselves. They may go out for a meal because they want to experience different food. They may go out for a drink in order to meet friends. They may go to the cinema to be entertained.

All these activities could be achieved at home far more cheaply—by cooking a meal in the kitchen, by buying a bottle of beer or wine from the off-licence, and by watching television or hiring a video—but what is it that makes people willing to spend more? One reason is that most people prefer to enjoy themselves in the company of others—so it is up to everyone working in the hotel, catering, leisure and tourism industry to make sure that these people continue to choose to go out. Without customers there would be no industry and no jobs

✱ FOR INTEREST

More restaurants, hotels and pubs are becoming aware of the importance of catering for families.

Theme parks based on the North American and European model are being built in Britain, for example Center Parc Sherwood Forest village, Thorpe Park and Chessington World of Adventure. They provide entertainment for all the family.

Multiplex cinemas with ten or more screens in the one building are growing in number in Britain. The accent is on a complete evening out, with family facilities and places to eat and drink.

Undercover shopping centres or malls usually have special café areas or foodcourts where shoppers can choose what to eat from a selection of several establishments, each of which often specialises in a single type of food, for instance, hamburgers, vegetarian food or pizzas.

As people live longer the number of privately run residential homes for the elderly is growing. Most employ medical staff as well as domestic staff.

More than half the pubs in Britain now serve food as well as alcoholic drinks. Since the new licensing act of 1988, many are open all day.

Conference centres are being built in country areas where delegates are able to combine leisure pursuits such as fitness training, walking, fishing, golf and squash with their business activities.

Universities and colleges now offer their facilities to conference delegates and holiday makers while students are away on vacation.

Catering establishments are taking notice of the nation's increasing awareness of eating healthy food. Menus now offer an interesting choice of low calorie, low fat, vegetarian and wholemeal dishes. Pubs too now serve more and more low calorie, low alcohol and non-alcoholic drinks, including beers and wines.

▶ ▶ ▶ TO DO

Next time you visit an establishment, perhaps a take-away, pub or sports centre, take a good look at the premises and the staff. What impression do you get? Is the place clean? What is the attitude of the staff? What do you think the standards of safety and hygiene are, and how could they be improved? Discuss your views with any friends or colleagues who have been to the same establishment.

All customers have the right to demand that the establishments they use are safe, secure and hygienic

Stand outside any popular pub or leisure centre, or outside a hospital, and it soon becomes clear why it is especially important to have tried and tested safety and security procedures, not just in emergencies such as an outbreak of fire or a bomb alert, but also in the day to day running of any establishment.

Customers, who perhaps visit a hotel, swimming pool, cinema or hospital only once, cannot be expected to know in detail its rules and regulations on safety. This is where staff and management come in. They will have had the time and training to equip them in avoiding any danger or risk, or in dealing with any problem that should arise. It is their responsibility, as the ones who work in the establishment, to make sure that everyone on the premises, whether they be customers, colleagues, contract workers or management, feel themselves and their possessions to be safe and secure.

Nearly all accidents, and most thefts, happen as a result of human error. A floor polisher flex may have been left trailing by a member of staff, a chef may overheat the fat fryer which bursts into flames and burns someone, or the pool attendant may not be as vigilant as usual, resulting in a swimmer requiring mouth-to-mouth resuscitation at the pool side. All these accidents can be avoided if proper care is taken. Of course, the fault in many accidents and thefts can be traced to the customers as well. But this does not lessen the responsibilities staff have towards all others in their care.

> ### What happens if safety standards drop
> - injuries and even deaths
> - fines or imprisonment
> - loss of jobs
> - customers stop coming
> - establishment forced to close
> - employer has licence taken away
> - reputation of establishment suffers
> - expensive battles in court

There are three main reasons why staff are responsible for safety:

- because the law requires it
- because they have a moral obligation
- because customers would cease to come to an establishment if it was not safe.

> ### When staff should take extra care
> - using dangerous equipment/utensils
> - using cleaning agents
> - cooking, especially with hot fat
> - disposing of rubbish
> - disposing of cigarette ends
> - anticipating trouble/violence
> - front of house security
> - lifting heavy weights
> - fire drill practice
> - washing floors
> - spills
> - customers claim lost property
> - locking doors and windows
> - electrical equipment
> - disposing of broken glass/crockery
> - handing out keys to hotel guests

Banquet in the Guildhall, London for President Mitterrand

The law

The industry is required by law to meet minimum safety standards, which cover the design of buildings, fire and security systems, furnishings and fittings, staff training, equipment, and facilities for both customers and staff. While the employer is the person responsible in most of these instances, staff have a legal responsibility as well, for instance in the way they use equipment provided. It is not just management who can be found guilty in a court of law, so can staff.

Rubbish and spills, if left around, can cause fire or injury

Everyone working in hotels, catering, leisure and tourism has a moral, commercial and legal obligation to ensure that standards of hygiene are kept high.

It is not just kitchen and restaurant staff preparing and serving food who have to take care—because contamination can lead to food poisoning—but non-food areas can also be health risks. The dangers of AIDS and Legionnaires' disease have reinforced the need for housekeeping staff to be vigilant against the spread of harmful bacteria when washing linen, for instance, or cleaning toilets and bathrooms. And standards of hygiene in hospitals have to be especially high, not only in operating theatres where everything has to be sterilised, but also in wards where patients, who are sick and weak, have low resistance to harmful bacteria.

There is also the threat of infestation by rats, mice, cockroaches and other bacteria-carrying pests, which are attracted to unhygienic surroundings where food and warmth are easy to find.

Because human beings also carry bacteria, it is important that staff pay attention to their own personal hygiene. Housekeeping staff who clean toilets and bathrooms, and kitchen and restaurant staff who handle food, need to keep themselves and their clothes spotless, and to wash their hands frequently. If staff are ill they should report this to their supervisor immediately because it is illegal to continue working when suffering from certain diseases. Also anyone who is unwell, for whatever reason, is putting his or her colleagues and customers at risk. Any sores, cuts or spots should be properly covered with a dressing.

This insistence on high standards—backed by the full force of law, commercial common sense and moral obligations—exists for a very good reason: the health and welfare of everyone on the premises. Poor hygienic practices which encourage the spread of disease can make anyone who uses an establishment very ill, and sometimes can even kill. This is because harmful bacteria, and other microorganisms which cause disease, thrive in unclean areas.

A lot of thought now goes into the design of equipment, for the sake of hygiene. Surfaces in kitchens, bathrooms and restaurants are made of hard materials such as steel, porcelain and plastic with as few nooks and crannies as possible to discourage bacteria from breeding. The accent is on straight, clean lines

Most bacteria are killed at temperatures above 70–75°C (158–167°F) provided they are kept at this temperature for long enough. Bed linen, towels and cleaning and drying cloths should be laundered at these high temperatures

Cleaning removes visible dust and dirt making an area or item look attractive. But it also removes bacteria which are invisible

How bacteria thrive

These microscopic living organisms, often called germs, exist almost everywhere. Some are harmless, but others can cause serious illness and even death, and extra care is needed to keep them in check. Fortunately, normal cleaning procedures within an establishment are usually adequate to deal with them, but all bacteria multiply quickly, and they thrive best in warm, moist, dirty surroundings such as drains, toilets and beds, where they feed on minute particles in the unclean environment. Raw food such as meat and fish also provides an ideal home for bacteria if left in warm conditions, for example at room temperature.

How to control the spread of bacteria

This can be achieved in a variety of ways:

- *removing* by thorough cleaning
- *killing* by heating, as in cooking, washing up, and laundering
- *killing* by using chemical disinfectants such as bleach
- *slowing up reproduction rate* by freezing and refrigerating
- *keeping out* by covering up.

Cross-contamination

This is the spread of bacteria from one surface to another, and is to be avoided at all costs. A knife or board which has been used to cut raw meat should not be used again until it has been thoroughly cleaned. A basin may look clean when it has been wiped with a cloth, but if the cloth has been used earlier for wiping the toilet seat it is likely to leave harmful bacteria in the basin. If hands are not washed regularly, particularly after blowing the nose, smoking, eating, or using the toilet, then bacteria will be carried to everything that is touched afterwards. Special clothing is often issued to staff working in areas of high risk, such as operating theatres, to minimise the chances of cross-contamination.

✱ FOR INTEREST

Bacteria are minute organisms which live in soil, water, plants, human beings and animals. Some bacteria are useful and necessary—those found in cheese and yogurt for instance, or in the intestines of animals and human beings to help digestion. Others are relatively harmless but cause food to go mouldy, soft or discoloured. But certain types of bacteria are very dangerous. They can make people ill through food poisoning, and in certain cases can cause death, for instance through Legionnaires' disease which can be caught from faulty air-conditioning and heating systems, and salmonella which infects some eggs, chickens and fish. Unfortunately the presence of these bacteria is not usually obvious until it is too late, because they are so small and cannot be seen without a microscope.

▶ ▶ ▶ TO DO

Make a list of examples of unhygienic practice which could cause bacteria to spread. If you work or study in the housekeeping department, confine your list to this area, if your interest lies in the preparation of food, make your list on examples of bad practice in the kitchen, and so on. Discuss your findings with colleagues, and against each example of bad practice write down what you think the correct practice should be.

Everyone has a responsibility to look clean, fresh and tidy in front of customers and work colleagues.

Customers will not enjoy being served food by someone who has dirty hands, for example, or who smells. They are most likely to be thinking that the food has also been unhygienically prepared—and they will probably be right. The appearance of staff is usually a fair indication of the standards of hygiene behind the scenes.

So it is important to maintain high personal standards of cleanliness, not only for the sake of appearance but also to protect customers against food poisoning and the spread of disease. Dirt and unhygienic working methods make the eating of food unsafe as well as unpleasant. Taking a shower or using a toilet can also be dangerous to health if these are not kept clean.

Presenting a hygienic and attractive appearance means keeping your body and clothes clean and fresh-looking, dressing appropriately, living a healthy life-style and making sure that you do your work in a safe and hygienic way.

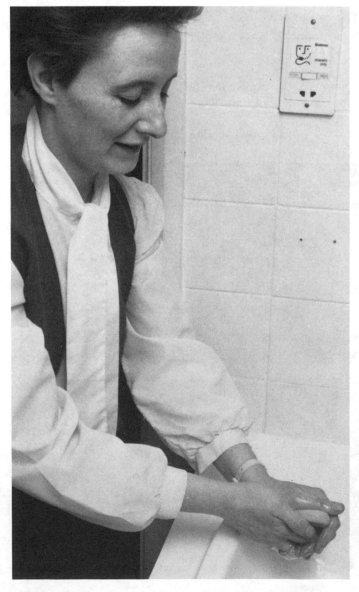

> ### ▶ ▶ ▶ TO DO
>
> Consider your daily freshness routine. Are there things you could do to improve your personal freshness? Do you need some advice? Ask the company nurse or doctor, or your own doctor for help. Take a look at the products on the market for hair and body care to check you are using those which suit you best.
>
> What rules relate to your personal cleanliness at work? Make your own summary of the main points.

Fingernails and hands These are always on show so they should be kept clean at all times. It is especially important to wash hands:

- immediately before handling and serving food
- after carrying out any cleaning activities or handling rubbish or other waste material
- before handling clean linen, cutlery, crockery or glassware
- after using the toilet
- after blowing your nose or sneezing or handling your hair.

Nails should be trimmed and kept clean. Although many establishments do not insist, it is preferable not to wear nail polish on duty unless you are working in an area such as reception.

Smokers should take special care that their hands are clean, as nicotine can stain the fingers.

Any wound should be covered with a clean dressing. If possible it should be the waterproof variety and food preparation staff should wear dressings that are coloured blue.

A clean body The importance of bodily freshness cannot be over-emphasised. The body secretes moisture constantly through sweat glands all over it. Sweat itself is virtually odourless and normally evaporates quickly. The smell comes from the bacteria which live on the perspiration, especially in areas such as the underarms where it cannot evaporate freely. A daily bath or shower is the best protection.

If staff are working under pressure or in a hot environment they will perspire more. It may be useful to use a deodorant to help prevent body odour.

A clear complexion Staff who look unhealthy will do little to advertise the health standards of the establishment they are working for. A clean skin and complexion depend largely on adequate sleep, exercise and a balanced diet. A healthy person will also be more capable of carrying out the job.

Beards and moustaches should be kept clean and trimmed. If clean-shaven, care should be taken to shave just before going on duty. A shadow always looks untidy.

Make-up should be used sparingly and be appropriate to the job. A little make-up is often useful to enhance a tired face.

Mouth   It is important to brush teeth and to ensure that breath is fresh. There are three major causes of bad breath:

Diet—heavily spiced food, garlic and alcohol can affect your breath. It is better to avoid such items just before going on duty, but if you suspect you have a problem, use a breath freshener. Chewing a mint will only vaguely mask the smell.

Smoking—the smell of tobacco lingers on the breath. It is advisable to clean teeth and rinse the mouth before returning to work after smoking.

Health—a stomach disorder or dental problem may cause bad breath. Regular visits to the dentist and attention to health and diet will normally avoid any problems.

Hair   In food preparation and service areas, long flowing hair is not acceptable for reasons of hygiene. It is also dangerous for anyone handling cleaning machines and similar equipment in which long hair could be trapped. Many establishments insist that hair is kept in a net or covered by a hat.

Unless the management requires an unusual hairstyle to present a particular image, then hairstyles worn at work should be kept as simple as possible.

Whatever the appropriate style, hair should always be kept clean and in a healthy condition. Hair absorbs smoke and food smells and it may be necessary to wash it daily. Regular brushing or combing will help towards a clean and tidy appearance.

Feet   In hotels and catering, staff are often required to be on their feet for long periods. It is therefore especially important to take care of the feet for reasons of health, hygiene and comfort.

They should be washed every day and toe nails should be kept trimmed. Socks, stockings or tights should be changed daily.

Ill health   When a member of staff has a cold or is feeling unwell, it is better for him or her to stay away from work than risk infecting other staff or customers. Bacteria can be transmitted quickly.

‼ REMEMBER

- Never lick your fingers.
- Keep your hands really clean.
- After washing, dry your hands using a hot air dryer, disposable paper towels or an automatic towel dispenser.
- Never dry your hands on an apron, dish or glass drying cloth or guest towel.
- Avoid touching your hair or scratching your head: if you have to, wash your hands immediately afterwards.
- Protect cuts and grazes with a clean dressing.
- Avoid using a handkerchief in the kitchen and public areas.
- Wash your hands after blowing your nose or sneezing.
- Do not eat, drink or chew while on duty.
- Never smoke on duty.
- Never touch food on the plates.
- Never touch the rims of clean glasses or cups or the area of plates on which food will be placed.

Perfume and after-shave

They should not be used in food preparation areas as they may taint the food. Where perfume or after-shave is permitted, only a small amount should be used

---

‼ REMEMBER

Long nails	can collect dirt and bacteria
Rings	make it difficult to wash your hands properly and jewellery can provide a home for bacteria
Open cuts and sores	are likely to contain bacteria which will get transferred to food and other surfaces
The mouth, lips, nose and hair	are also likely to be contaminated by bacteria and when these parts of your body are touched some bacteria will get transferred to your hands, the handkerchief, the rim of the cup or glass etc. and from there can contaminate food and other surfaces.

Whether a uniform is provided by the establishment or the staff are expected to wear their own clothes, clothing should:

- be clean and fresh—all clothes should be changed frequently, especially underclothing and shirts or blouses. Clean clothes should be ironed and mended as necessary.
- be hygienic—especially in housekeeping, food preparation and food and drink service areas. Most establishments require staff working in these areas to wear a suitable overall or uniform as these are designed to be hygienic and strong enough to be washed frequently.
- be comfortable and practical—clothes should fit properly. Flowing sleeves or trailing bows are dangerous when using machinery, and unhygienic when handling food.
- allow for free movement—staff need to be able to bend and stretch easily. Clothing which restricts movement is dangerous.
- look good—staff are a direct advertisement to customers of the standards of the establishment.
- be appropriate to the establishment—formal clothes should be worn in a formal establishment, but if the atmosphere is more relaxed, staff may be requested to wear casual clothes.

Uniforms

In some catering establishments certain staff are required to wear uniforms. These may contribute to the atmosphere and theme which the owners or management wish to portray to the customers. They may also provide protection to staff and save wear and tear on the employees' own clothes.

A uniform should be kept clean and tidy, and should be practical, durable and easy to maintain.

Non-work clothes should be kept in the staff room or in a suitable cupboard or locker. Kitchen and restaurant staff should never leave their clothes in a room where food is stored and handled (unless the clothes are kept in a cupboard or locker provided for the purpose).

Safety clothes

Where staff are working with machinery or with hot equipment, uniforms are worn for safety and protection.

Some cleaning tasks require staff to wear special gauntlets to protect their hands. Rubber gloves should also be provided for staff working with cleaning agents to prevent skin irritations and the spread of bacteria.

Some establishments provide safety shoes to be worn in the kitchens and maintenance departments. These protect the feet from heavy weights or harmful substances.

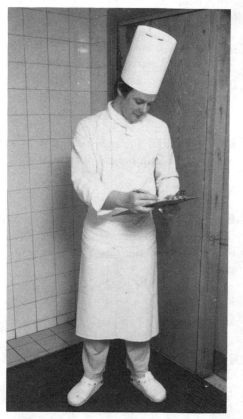

Safety clothing is provided for a reason—to protect the wearer. It is important therefore to wear it correctly. A chef's uniform is not complete without a long white apron, which is not for wiping the hands but to protect against hot spills and splashes

Many staff spend the major part of their working hours on their feet, so comfortable, practical shoes are essential.

- It is important that shoes have non-slip soles, especially for staff involved in food preparation, service or cleaning jobs, where they are required to carry heavy items and the floors may become slippery.
- Heels should be of a practical height, usually no higher than 35 mm (1½ inches).
- Open-toed shoes should not be worn in case there is an accident. A sturdy pair of shoes will protect the feet from hot liquids and dropped plates and knives.
- When lace-up shoes are worn, the laces should be tied carefully at all times.
- Shoes should be kept clean and in good repair.
- If possible keep a second pair of shoes at work. Nothing relieves tired, aching feet quite like a change of footwear half-way through the working day!

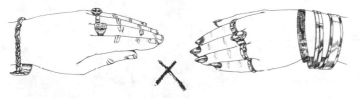

A lot of jewellery should be avoided. It will get in the way, will distract customers and may be dangerous or unhygienic. Staff who handle food are allowed to wear a plain wedding ring, but no other jewellery.

Why wear a uniform—some examples

Kitchen staff	
Hat	To keep hair away from food, to discourage scratching the head and for comfort (a hat keeps the head cooler).
Double fronted white jacket	To protect the body from heat and spills. White so that it does not absorb heat, to show up dirt and so encourage frequent laundering.
Long apron and trousers	To protect legs from spills and heat.
Safety shoes	To protect feet from hot spills, and dropped items, such as knives.
Reception staff	
Cotton blouse/shirt	To look cool and fresh, easily laundered.
Neat skirt	Long enough to be decent when sitting or bending.
Comfortable shoes	For standing for long periods, safe for walking.
Cleaners	
Cotton overall, loose fit	To protect from splashes with cleaning fluids, and to allow easy movement when stretching and bending.
Rubber gloves	To protect hands from cleaning fluids.
Flat comfortable shoes	For long hours working on the feet.

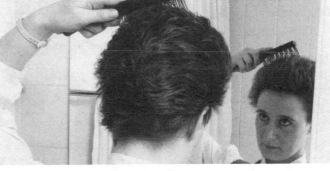

▶ ▶ ▶ TO DO

Think of the hotel, catering, leisure and tourism establishments you know and find as many examples as you can of their staff who wear while they are on duty:

- uniform
- their own clothes
- special safety clothing.

Against your list note any special reasons for what they wear. If you are doing this activity with others, divide the discussion so different people concentrate on finding examples of each of the groups of clothing.

6 THE IMPRESSION YOU GIVE

Whether a uniform or staff's own clothes are worn, they should be properly looked after to:

- present a smart image to customers
- prolong the life of the clothes
- ensure safety and hygiene.

Looking after clothes includes storing them carefully when they are not being worn.

Trousers, skirts, dresses, overalls and jackets should be hung up on clothes hangers to avoid unnecessary creasing which damages the fibres of the clothes and makes them look scruffy.

Freshly laundered and ironed shirts may be hung up on hangers or carefully folded and placed in a drawer.

Items such as cardigans, pullovers and scarves should be folded neatly to minimise creasing.

Pockets

Pockets are for holding items essential to the job such as note pads and pens. They are not for holding any old item.

- Cramming tissues or other items into a pocket will cause a garment to lose its shape.
- Avoid placing pens in pockets unless the caps are firmly in place, or ink leaks may occur.
- Loose coins may cause a pocket to wear thin. Use a purse to carry change.

▶ ▶ ▶ **TO DO**

Ask someone at work or home to show you how to sew on a button and repair the hem of your skirt or the turn-up on your trousers.

Alternatively or in addition

Take three bits of old material (preferably cotton). Stain one with ink, the second with ball-point ink and the third with tea or coffee. Then remove the stain using the appropriate stain remover.

‼ REMEMBER

Loose hems are dangerous, they may catch on heels and result in a fall. Check regularly that hems are properly sewn up and repair them immediately they come undone.

Clothing should be worn properly fastened for reasons of safety and appearance. Lost buttons should be replaced. Broken zips should be repaired.

Shoes should be kept clean and in good repair. Worn soles and heels are slippery and may result in a fall. They should either be replaced or reheeled and soled regularly. Broken laces can also cause a fall if they are not replaced.

Washing clothes

Clothing will remain attractive and hygienic if it is regularly washed and changed. There are several simple rules to be followed when washing or laundering garments:

- Read the label giving washing instructions on the garment.
- Sort clothes according to the recommended wash.
- Soak if necessary to remove stains, but never soak wool or silk.
- Wash coloured clothes separately unless sure that the dye will not run. Check that the garment is colour-fast by placing a small section in water first.
- Use a soap which is suitable for the type of fabric being washed and enough to clean the item effectively. Some soaps are best for hand-washing, others for machine-washing.
- Rinse thoroughly.
- Fabric conditioner may be used to restore softness and to get rid of any remaining soap.
- Wash clothes frequently. Dirt builds up in the fibres, and may be hard to remove if left for a long time.
- Treat stains quickly.

Rules of stain removal

1. Deal with all stains as soon as possible. Once a stain has hardened or has seeped into a surface, it will be much more difficult to remove.
2. Try to identify the stain and the surface:
   - Note the appearance. Stains caused by pastes or thick liquids, such as paint, nail varnish, mud etc., are solid looking and caked on the surface of the fabric. Some stains caused by liquids, such as wine or tea, penetrate the material.
   - Feel the stain. Hardness may indicate lacquer or glue, while brittle stains could be sugar compounds (these often turn white when scratched). Some stains, such as new paint or toffee, are tacky.
   - Note the colour. Many stains have characteristic colours—blood is red but becomes brown with age, and may even look black.
   - Note the odour. Certain stains, such as perfume and salad dressing, have characteristic odours. All odours are more apparent when steam is applied.
3. Remove as much of the stain as possible before using any other treatment, but avoid rubbing it. If the stain is solid, gently scrape away the hardened build-up; if the excess is liquid, use an absorbent cloth to mop it up.
4. Always test the effect of any stain removal agent first, by applying to a part of the surface which cannot be seen.
5. Always use the mildest treatment first. Start with cold water if you are not sure about the type of stain, because hot water or detergent may set the stain and make it impossible to remove.
6. Always treat the stain from the outer edges and work inwards, so as to avoid spreading it and making it larger.
7. If the stain is persistent, then try a harsher treatment, but avoid hard rubbing or using strong stain removal agents.
8. After cleaning, thoroughly rinse the stained area with cold water.
9. Leave the area as dry as possible.

PRACTICAL TIPS

Treat stains as quickly as possible and try the weaker stain removers first (they are listed below in order of strength).

Ball point pen ink: 1. methylated spirits, 2. paint remover, 3. hydrogen peroxide

Blood: 1. cold water, 2. ammonia, 3. hydrogen peroxide, 4. rust remover

Chewing gum: trichloroethylene

Coffee or tea: 1. water, 2. acetic acid, 3. hydrogen peroxide

Egg: 1. soap, 2. digester

Ink (blue or black): 1. warm water with pads to absorb loosened colour, 2. ammonia, 3. hydrofluoric acid

Lipstick or nail varnish: amyl acetate

Perspiration: 1. warm water, 2. ammonia, 3. acetic acid, 4. hydrogen peroxide

Scorch: hydrogen peroxide.

In order to provide the high standards of health, hygiene and safety that customers expect and the law requires, it is necessary for staff to be methodical and efficient in their work. If they are punctual, helpful and aware of the needs of customers and colleagues, and they understand the aims of the establishment, standards of hygiene and safety are more likely to be high. In other words, staff must really care about the service they provide to ensure the health and safety of everyone who uses the premises—customers, colleagues and management alike.

Customers with special needs

People who are elderly, disabled or very young may have special requirements which staff should be aware of. For example, a customer in a wheelchair must have easy access to his or her room, the restaurant and the lavatory. A toddler may need a high chair and a special children's menu. The aim is to maintain as normal a service as possible while still catering to people's particular needs.

Coping with pressure

When staff are very busy there is a great temptation to drop standards in order to complete all the necessary tasks. If staff use the most efficient methods of doing things in the first place, standards are more likely to remain high, and a tendency to panic, which never helps, will be avoided.

Working as a team

Each member of staff is dependent on others if tasks are to be completed to a high standard. These colleagues may work in the same department, or they may be in another section altogether. Exactly how staff teams are organised depends on the size and type of establishment. A small restaurant may only employ two people to carry out all the duties, from cooking the food to taking payment. A large hotel, leisure centre or hospital may employ 100 people or more, from pool attendants to housekeeping staff, with each person responsible for a different task. In large organisations it is particularly important to have a good working relationship with other departments. For instance, it is a waste of effort for domestic staff in a hospital to start cleaning the wards before the nurses have made the beds. The efficient way is to wait until the beds are made and the dust has settled. Whatever the size and type of establishment, a little thought about how and when tasks should be done to best fit in with the work schedules of other colleagues will go a long way towards achieving the desired results.

‼ REMEMBER

If you are ill or unavoidably late for work, phone in as soon as possible so that the necessary arrangements can be made to cover for your absence.

Timing

One of the most valuable skills to learn in the industry is that of timing, especially in catering. For instance kitchen and restaurant staff should be able to estimate the time it will take to cook and serve a meal and for the customers to eat it. Otherwise customers will feel rushed or, if service is slow, that they have been forgotten. In this example, staff should be familiar with food preparation times so that courses can be served appropriately staggered to minimise delays, and so that all customers at one table are served with a course at the same time. Bad timing can lead not only to unhygienic presentation and poor working methods, but also to resentment among other staff. When staff are under this sort of stress accidents often happen, especially in kitchens where potentially hazardous equipment is used.

Punctuality

Staff have a responsibility to customers and colleagues to arrive at work on time. If people turn up late for duty it means that other staff members will have to cover for them, leading to resentment and delays. Standards of hygiene and safety are almost bound to suffer as a result.

Avoiding waste

Staff can avoid wasting resources such as gas and electricity, food and equipment by making sure that:

- All appliances are turned off when not in use, for example coffee machines, plate warmers, floor cleaning machines, hot water taps, all of which can cause accidents to any unsuspecting person.
- Food portions are correctly measured, neither too large nor too small.
- The rules of stock control are properly adhered to (first in, first out). It is dangerous (because it can lead to food poisoning) and illegal to serve food which is past its 'use by' date.
- Equipment is used correctly and maintained in good order.

Communicating with others

Communicating well with customers and other staff is essential if standards are to remain high. Misunderstandings through poor communication between people leads to inferior service and sometimes accidents. For instance a customer or colleague could be badly hurt by slipping on a wet floor because no written or verbal warning was given. It is important for staff to explain clearly what their intentions are and to listen closely to information or instructions from customers, colleagues and management. In this way everyone will understand exactly what is required.

◆ ◆ ◆ TO DO

Think of further examples of when timing is important, one for each of the following situations:

- barstaff working in a busy pub or a cocktail bar
- housekeeping staff cleaning a guest suite or a hospital ward
- reception staff on duty in a conference centre or a hotel
- banqueting staff serving a dinner in a civic hall or the VIP marquee at an agricultural show.

You may find it helpful to discuss likely situations with people who work or have worked in any areas you are unfamiliar with.

‼ REMEMBER

- Keep the message, whether verbal or written, brief and to the point.
- Use commonly understood words.
- Time the message appropriately, for instance do not ask the chef a question when he is lifting a heavy pan out of the oven, or the waitress what the special of the day is when she is about to greet some customers who have just arrived.
- Pay attention to what is said in reply.
- Ask for the message to be repeated if you have not understood it properly.
- Write down important messages and read them back to the person who is giving them to make sure you have understood correctly.

In hotel, catering, leisure and tourism occupations, hours are often irregular and the work is strenuous. A healthy diet, exercise and enough sleep will help those working in the industry carry out their jobs effectively and well.

What the human body needs

In order to grow and function properly the body needs a variety of nutrients. There are six groups of essential nutrients.

1. Carbohydrates

Sugar and starch, both carbohydrates, provide energy. Sugar comes in various forms: sucrose (used to make white and brown sugar and found in many sweet and savoury processed foods, chocolate, cakes and biscuits), lactose (found in milk), maltose (which occurs in malt and is also produced by the body when starch is being digested), glucose and fructose (both occur naturally in honey and many sweet fruits).

Starch is found in potatoes, pulses such as lentils, chick peas and kidney beans, breakfast cereals and other cereal products such as flour, rice, bread and pasta.

Cellulose (found in pulses, brown rice, wholemeal flour, fruit and vegetables) and pectin (found in ripe fruit) are also carbohydrates but they cannot be digested. They are necessary because they provide dietary fibre—or bulk—which is one of the things that helps the whole system work properly and prevents disease.

2. Protein

Protein is needed for the formation and replacement of brain cells, muscle cells, skin cells and the many other cells which make up the human body.

Adults need between 60 to 80 grams (about 3 oz) of protein per day. All natural foods contain some protein, but it is particularly concentrated in meat, fish, cheese, eggs, nuts and pulses (especially soya beans). Protein-rich foods like meat and cheese also contain a lot of saturated fat, so it is best for the protein in a person's diet to come from a variety of sources.

Protein which is not required for growth or repair of the body cells is used as energy.

3. Fats and oils

Fats and oils are the most concentrated source of energy—the only difference between them is that fats are solid at room temperature whereas oils are liquid. (Some oils, for example those used to make margarine, are processed to become solid.)

Besides products like butter, margarine, lard, dripping and cooking or salad oils, other foods high in fat are cheese, cream, egg yolk, oily fish, nuts and many cuts of meat. However white fish, turkey, chicken, egg white, cottage cheese and bread are relatively low in fat.

There is a lot of evidence that eating too much fat leads to health problems (see unit 9).

4. Vitamins

Vitamins are substances of various sorts that the body cannot make for itself, but which it needs in small amounts so that it can function properly. (The exception is vitamin D which the body makes when direct sunlight falls on the skin.)

Serious vitamin deficiency diseases are unusual in Britain because for most people a wide range of food is easily available, but it is still possible to go short of a vitamin (see box). For example someone who doesn't eat fresh fruit or vegetables, or always eats overcooked vegetables, will not get enough vitamin C or folic acid.

Vitamin A or retinol
Occurs in cheese, milk, cream, butter, margarine, eggs and liver. Also apricots and spinach. Carrots and dark green vegetables contain carotene which is converted to vitamin A in the liver.
Essential for the proper working of the protective mucous membranes which line the nose and throat and other body cavities open to the external environment, and for vision in dim light.

Vitamin B1 or thiamine
Occurs in a variety of foods but good sources are wholegrain cereals, pork, bacon, eggs, kidney and liver.
Essential for controlling the release of energy from glucose in the diet.

Vitamin B2 (contains riboflavin)
Occurs in liver, kidneys, cheese, milk, eggs and yeast extracts.
Essential for the proper functioning of muscles, so it is especially important for athletes or people doing hard physical work.

Niacin
Occurs in liver, kidneys, sardines.
Essential for healthy skin.

Vitamin C or ascorbic acid
Occurs in blackcurrants, strawberries, blackberries, green peppers, cabbage, cauliflower, potatoes, Brussels sprouts, oranges and lemons.
Essential for healthy connective tissue.

Vitamin D
Occurs in oily fish, fish oils, margarine and eggs.
Helps calcium to be absorbed properly (which keeps teeth and bones healthy).

Vitamin E
Occurs in vegetable oils, cereals, eggs.
Helps maintain and protect membranes and is believed to be important for fertility.

Vitamin K
Occurs in vegetables.
Essential for blood clotting.

Folic acid
Occurs in liver and kidneys, raw green vegetables (however it is easily destroyed in cooking), and many other foods.
Prevents some forms of anaemia.

5. Minerals

Like vitamins, minerals are needed in quite small amounts. They help with a number of different functions in the body (see box).

The most common mineral deficiency disease in Britain is anaemia—a lack of iron. A great many people, particularly women, suffer from this form of anaemia—the main symptoms are tiredness and listlessness. Pregnant women are often advised to take iron tablets. Vitamin C helps the body to take in iron from food.

It is possible to have too much of a mineral. The most common example of this is sodium (common salt)—see unit 9.

6. Water

Although some people do not think of it as a nutrient, water is essential for life. About 70% of a person's body weight is made up of water, but in a reasonable diet it is quite easy to get this. A lot of food has a high water content and most people drink sufficient beverages or water during the day as part of their normal routine.

Overweight/underweight?

In order to be healthy, it is important that a person's weight is appropriate to his or her height.

The amount of energy the body requires depends on the rate at which that person's body burns the energy. This will depend on how much physical activity is taken, on age, size and whether the person is a man or woman.

There are two main uses of energy:

- The basic functions which the body must be able to do or it will die, like breathing, making new cells, heart beating.
- Physical activity like walking, running and sport.

In a healthy adult of the right weight, energy input should balance energy output. If too much food and drink is taken or the diet is not balanced, the excess energy will be stored as fat (adipose tissue) and once this has formed, it is very difficult to get rid of.

Iron
Occurs in red meat and offal, bread, shellfish and some vegetables.
Essential for the production of haemoglobin, the oxygen-carrying part of blood.

Calcium
Occurs in milk and milk products, small fish (if the bones are eaten), bread and some cereals. Calcium cannot be absorbed without vitamin D.
Essential for healthy bones and teeth.

Phosphorus
Occurs in most foods.
Essential for healthy bones and teeth.

Sodium
Occurs in salt, bacon, ham and some processed foods.
Essential for nerve and muscle action. Regulates body fluids.

Measuring energy value of food
The energy value of food is measured in calories (cal) or the standard international unit called a Joule (J). As these are tiny units (one Joule equals 4.2 calories), energy value is more often measured in kilocalories (kcal) or kilojoules (kJ).

▶ ▶ ▶ **TO DO**

Firstly
Have a look at a chart or table which shows what weight you should be for your height. (You will find one in most books on healthy eating or nutrition, your doctor can help and the Health Education Council publishes a chart on ideal body weight.)

If you are underweight you will probably need to eat a bit more. Go for well-balanced, nutritious foods, don't try and fill up on fatty or sugary foods. If you are very underweight see your doctor.

If you are overweight you should try and lose weight. Aim to lose ½ to 1 kg (1 to 2 lbs) a week. Cut down on fat, sugar and alcohol and eat more high-fibre foods. Take regular exercise.

Secondly
Make a careful note of everything you have to eat and drink over the next three days (start your records so you include one day off from work or study). At the end of the period compare what you have eaten with the recommended sources of nutrients in this unit and units 9 and 10. Ask yourself:

- Have I had a balanced diet?
- What foods should I eat more of?
- What foods and drinks should I consume less of?

Repeat the exercise in three or four months time and at similar intervals until you are fairly sure you are following a consistently balanced diet.

9 YOUR HEALTH

It is not enough merely to include all essential nutrients in the diet. As a nation the British are inclined to eat too much, or too little, of certain foods, which research has shown to be unhealthy.

For a healthy diet
- Cut down on fat, sugar and salt.
- Eat plenty of fibre-rich foods.
- Eat plenty of fresh fruit and vegetables.
- Attempt to cut down the amount of convenience and processed food eaten, or choose convenience foods that are high in fibre, low in sugar, salt and fat.
- Limit the amount of alcohol consumed.

> ▶ ▶ ▶ **TO DO**
> Visit your local supermarket and examine the labels on the packets and tins of five foods that you frequently eat. Note whether any of these are labelled low in fat, salt and sugar, or high in fibre. If they are not, what healthier substitutes are available?

Fat

Fats may be saturated, monounsaturated or polyunsaturated. The distinction lies in how the hydrogen molecules, which all fats contain, are arranged (its chemical make-up).

There is now a lot of evidence that eating too much fat leads to health problems. This is partly because it can make people overweight, which is always unhealthy, and partly because saturated fats can increase the level of cholesterol in the blood and a high cholesterol level can lead to heart disease. Monounsaturated fats are much less likely to cause problems, and polyunsaturated fats are thought to be the most healthy alternative.

Cut down on fat
- Choose a low fat polyunsaturated spread or vegetable margarine rather than butter.
- Use skimmed or semi-skimmed milk rather than full cream milk.
- Choose low fat yogurt instead of cream, or where cream must be used, use single rather than double.
- Limit the intake of high fat cheese, such as cheddar, and substitute by lower fat hard cheese, such as Edam, or cottage or curd cheese.
- Grill or bake food rather than frying it.
- If it is necessary to fry food, use polyunsaturated oils, such as sunflower or soya.

Food containing mainly saturated fat
milk
butter
cream
most cheeses
meat and meat products
lard and dripping
hard margarines
palm and coconut oils
egg yolk

Food containing mainly poly-unsaturated fat
fish
nuts
game
wild fowl
most soft margarine
corn oil
sunflower oil
safflower oil
soya oil

Food containing mainly mono-unsaturated fat
poultry
groundnut oil
olive oil

Sugar

Sugar provides no nutrients at all, and is not necessary as part of a healthy diet. Sufficient energy is provided by other foods that contain nutrients.

Sugar therefore contributes nothing to the diet, apart from unnecessary calories, and causes tooth decay.

Cut down on sugar
- Try to cut down on the amount of sugar taken in tea and coffee, or, better still, omit it altogether.
- Choose low-calorie soft drinks.
- Avoid cereals and canned foods containing a lot of sugar.
- Read food labels for hidden sugar.
- Reduce the amount of sugar in recipes.

Salt

Human beings need only a little salt to remain healthy. There is no need to add extra salt in cooking or on the plate because food already contains, naturally, as much salt as a person needs. Too much is unhealthy. High blood pressure can be reduced by eating less salt.

Cut down on salt

- Use less salt in cooking. Use fresh herbs and spices to add interesting flavours to the food.
- Resist the temptation to add salt to food after it has been prepared.
- Avoid heavily salted foods, such as nuts, crisps and salty bacon or meat.
- Cut down on convenience or processed foods which usually contain a lot of salt.
- Use convenience and other processed foods which are labelled low-salt.

Eat fewer biscuits, cakes and sweets, substitute with fresh fruit, dried fruit and unsalted nuts

---

PRACTICAL TIPS

for preserving vitamins in vegetables

- Use only good quality, very fresh vegetables and prepare them when you need them.
- Use a sharp knife—blunt knives are not only dangerous, but they will bruise the vegetables and cause loss of vitamin C.
- Never soak prepared vegetables in cold water. The exception is potatoes which will discolour unless they are placed directly into water after peeling.
- Place in boiling water and when the water re-boils, lower the heat so the liquid is gently bubbling—vigorous movement will damage the vegetables. Using already boiling water reduces the length of time the vegetables have to cook, so helping preserve vitamin C. Ignore the saying 'put root vegetables into cold water'—potatoes, for example are an important source of vitamin C in the average diet.
- Cover the pan with a lid during cooking. This means less water can be used and the vegetables are partly cooked in steam, so helping preserve vitamin C. Lift the lid from time to time during cooking to allow volatile acids (such as those created during the cooking of cauliflower, broccoli and Brussels sprouts) to escape.
- If possible, steam vegetables rather than boiling or frying them.
- Never cook vegetables in advance so they have to be kept warm. If vegetables have to be cooked in advance it is preferable to boil them briefly, cool under cold running water, chill until needed then reheat quickly in fresh boiling water.

Eat low fat meat, especially poultry, and fish instead of high fat red meat. Do not eat the skin of poultry as it is fatty

YOUR HEALTH

Fibre

Dietary fibre cannot be digested by the stomach and passes through the body almost unchanged. It absorbs water in the intestine and speeds up the passage of food, preventing constipation and stomach disorders.

Eat more fibre
- Eat at least four slices of bread each day, preferably wholemeal or high fibre white bread.
- Substitute wholemeal flour products for white flour products, for example wholemeal pastry, pasta and bread.
- Use more peas, beans and lentils in cooking. Baked beans are a good source of fibre.
- Eat more potatoes, especially with their skins. Yams, plantain, cassava and brown rice are also high-fibre foods.

Convenience foods

The term 'convenience food' is given to those foods which require little or no preparation. Not all convenience foods are highly processed or 'junk' foods, for example low-fat natural yogurt, tinned fish in water, and canned fruit in juice rather than syrup. Manufacturers have responded to public demand for low sugar, salt and fat products, and so wholesome convenience foods are available.

Many tins and packets of food now have labels giving details of the nutritional value of the item, as well as a list of ingredients. It is therefore important to read the labels on foods. Choose those which are:

- high in fibre
- low in sugar
- low in saturated fats
- low in salt
- low in additives
- high in polyunsaturated fats.

Eat at least one piece of fruit per day and plenty of fresh vegetables

20

Alcohol

Alcohol affects the nervous system connected to the brain, which controls a person's thoughts, movements and reactions. It is intoxicating and makes certain activities, such as driving a car, dangerous.

When alcohol is consumed, most of it is immediately absorbed into the bloodstream where it passes to the liver which uses most of it up. The body gets rid of the rest in sweat or urine.

How much alcohol is in the body depends on how much is drunk and on the height, weight and sex of the drinker. Drinking on an empty stomach can mean that alcohol is absorbed into the bloodstream more quickly.

On average it takes about one hour to expel each unit of alcohol from the body—a standard glass of wine, half a pint of beer, or a single measure of a spirit are each equivalent to one unit of alcohol. A person who has drunk three pints (six units) of beer, for example, will be affected by alcohol in his or her bloodstream for at least six hours afterwards.

Drink less alcohol

- For men the sensible limit is considered to be 21 units a week, for women 14 units a week, provided drinks are spread throughout the week.
- 36 or more units a week for men and 22 units or more for women are considered too much.
- There are times when it is safer not to drink alcohol at all, for instance before driving, or when pregnant, or if taking medication.
- Men who regularly drink over 50 units and women drinking over 36 units are almost certainly damaging their health and their personal lives.

‼ REMEMBER

Excessive drinking damages health. Too much can lead to legal and financial worries and problems in relationships. It can also have certain short-term and long-term effects.

hangovers	liver damage
loss of memory	stomach ulcers
violence	cancer of the throat
crime	brain damage
death	sexual difficulties
injuries	malnutrition
illness	depression
vomiting	high blood pressure

✳ FOR INTEREST

The legal limit for driving is 80 milligrams of alcohol in 100 millilitres of blood. But it's practically impossible to tell when you reach this level (unless a breathalyser is used) because it varies with the weight and sex of the drinker. Some may reach their limit after only three units, equivalent to $1\frac{1}{2}$ pints of beer or three single measures of a spirit. And some people's driving ability can be reduced drastically after just one or two drinks. Even if drivers are below the legal limit, they can still be prosecuted if a police officer thinks their driving has been affected by alcohol. The only way to be really sure is never to drink before you drive.

▶ ▶ ▶ TO DO

For the next seven days keep a careful (and honest!) record of what alcohol you drink. (If you don't drink alcohol at all, ask a friend who does to carry out this part of the exercise for you.)

Then calculate how many units of alcohol have been consumed in the period. One unit is equivalent to:

- one half pint of beer or lager (ordinary strength)
- one standard glass of wine
- one standard glass of sherry or port
- a single measure ($\frac{1}{6}$th gill) of a spirit such as whisky, gin, rum, vodka or brandy.

Work out if the total is within the sensible limit, or too much. If it is too much think of some alternative drinks which you (or your friend) could have, which would be as enjoyable in similar circumstances, but which contain less alcohol or none at all.

Regular exercise is as important to good health as a balanced diet. Exercise makes the body work better. It improves circulation, makes the heart more efficient, helps protect against heart disease, aids sleep and relaxation, and generally makes a person's working and private life more enjoyable.

Keep fit

Regular exercise helps people to keep fit. Fitness is a combination of suppleness, strength and stamina.

Suppleness—the ability to bend and stretch easily helps to prevent injury when tackling awkward jobs or lifting heavy objects.

Strength—strong muscles are needed for climbing stairs, lifting and carrying, and also for generally getting around. Strong muscles protect the body from strains and injury and help posture.

Stamina—in order to keep going through a strenuous day without feeling exhausted it is necessary to have stamina. Stiffness and pain can occur when muscles are not used regularly. By keeping fit, it is possible to avoid a lot of muscular pain.

Gentle exercise

It is best to take exercise that is enjoyable, and which can be fitted easily into the rest of life, so that it can become a regular routine.

It is a good idea to combine gentle exercise with other day-to-day activities:

- Walk up stairs, rather than using the lift.
- Always walk when possible, rather than taking a car, bus or train.

Begin gradually, walking a little further and faster than usual each day and building up until you have a satisfactory routine and are walking for at least half an hour each day.

More strenuous exercise

If you are at all worried about your health, then consult a doctor before starting an exercise programme.

The rule is to start gently and not to overdo it. A little soreness is inevitable for lazy muscles because it takes time to get back into condition.

There are many ways of taking exercise, alone, with friends or by joining a club:

Jogging—start very slowly over short distances, and build up distance and speed gradually. Wear proper running shoes, which support the feet, legs and ankles.

Exercise has to be regular to be effective

Get off the bus or train at an earlier stop than usual and walk the last part of your journey

> ▶ ▶ ▶ **TO DO**
>
> Think about the amount of regular exercise you take. How far do you walk every day? Do you take part in any sport? If you do not take any exercise, try to work out an exercise programme that will fit in with your daily life.

Cycling—will strengthen the leg muscles and is ideal as it can be combined with getting to work, doing the shopping or visiting friends.

Tennis and other racquet games—are good for the heart and lungs. Care should be taken not to overtax the muscles or cause injury to ligaments and tendons.

Posture

Good posture is an important part of overall fitness. A straight spine means strong back and stomach muscles which makes back pain, one of the most common causes of absence from work, less likely.

Relaxation

Learning how to relax properly is a fundamental part of keeping fit. Tension can cause back, neck and other muscle pains. The inability to relax can also result in lack of sleep.

Sleep

Everybody needs sleep if they are to function properly, both at work and at play. On average, adults require about 7½ hours sleep a night, although some need more and some feel healthy with a lot less. Missing a couple of hours sleep one night will not affect health, but over a long period lack of sleep affects concentration, and results in tiredness, irritability and eventually poor health.

Swimming is one of the best overall exercises, strengthening and increasing the suppleness of most of the muscles in the body

---

✳ FOR INTEREST

Deaths from heart disease in Britain occur at a rate of one every three minutes. As a country we are second in the world league table for heart disease mortality (Sweden is first).

Smoking is the greatest single cause of premature death in Britain. But fortunately more and more people are giving it up—an estimated 11 million people have given up smoking in recent years in England alone. This is good news for the non-smokers who cannot avoid breathing in other people's tobacco smoke in public and work areas.

?? HOW TO

Relax

1. Lie or sit in a comfortable position.
2. Close the eyes.
3. Take a deep breath and tense all the muscles in the body.
4. Hold the position for several seconds—feel the tension in the muscles.
5. Breathe out, relaxing the body at the same time. Let the breath go with a deep sigh and feel the tension seeping out of the muscles.
6. Consciously let each part of the body relax, starting with the feet and working all the way up to the head.
7. Try to relax so completely that the body feels as though it is sinking through the floor.
8. Lie completely relaxed for as long as is possible.

Everyone at work, from the most junior worker to the managers, proprietors, directors or governing authorities, is responsible for the health and safety of those around them.

The main piece of legislation covering health and safety at work is the Health and Safety at Work Act (1974), or HASAWA for short. Under the Act:

- Everyone at work and everyone affected by the work is protected.
- Employers and staff have a legal duty to look after the health and safety of their colleagues, trainees, customers, guests, visitors, members of the public, contractors and anyone else affected by their work. Self-employed people have the same duty, as do company directors, partners, proprietors and anyone else in overall charge.
- No-one must interfere with or misuse—intentionally or recklessly—anything required by the Act and provided in the interests of health, safety and welfare.

Employers and staff have other specific duties.

Everyone at work and everyone affected by the work is protected under HASAWA

Duties of the employer
1. To provide safe and healthy working conditions, including safe ways of getting into and out of the workplace, and make adequate arrangements for the welfare of staff (such as toilet, washing and rest facilities).
2. To ensure that equipment is safe to use and kept in good working order through regular cleaning and maintenance.
3. To provide safe systems for the use, handling, storage and transport of materials (such as cleaning agents, food and drink items, gas cylinders, etc.)
4. To ensure all staff know why and how to carry out safe practices. This will mean providing information, instruction and training (in languages other than English if necessary), establishing clear lines of responsibility and authority, and maintaining proper supervision.
5. If the employer has five or more employees, to provide a written statement or policy, describing the organisation and arrangements made for the health and safety of staff and to make sure that all staff know of and have ready access to this statement.

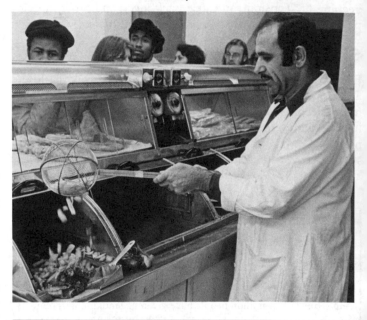

Duties of the staff
1. To take reasonable care of their own health and safety and that of other people who may be affected by what they do or fail to do.
2. To co-operate with the employer to maintain health and safety standards.

Who enforces HASAWA

Environmental health officers (EHOs) are responsible for making sure that the law is upheld in most of the hotel and catering industry. These officers are employed by the local authority. In factory canteens, sports and leisure clubs and arenas, theatres and cinemas, health and safety inspectors (HSIs) employed by the Health and Safety Executive, enforce the law.

▶ ▶ ▶   **TO DO**

Obtain a copy of the health and safety policy of a hotel, catering, leisure or tourism company of your choice. Find out how the company brings the policy to the attention of its staff and study the document to note:

- how the responsibility for health and safety is organised
- any arrangements for working with trade union-appointed safety representatives (see also unit 13)
- any particular hazards which are identified (for example use of particular equipment) and what precautions are recommended to deal with them
- arrangements for health and safety training
- other systems and procedures adopted to ensure a safe workplace
- the procedure for dealing with accidents
- how the policy is kept up-to-date.

At any reasonable time and without prior warning or the permission of anyone in control of the premises, the enforcing officer may enter any premises of the business or organisation to carry out an inspection.

If the officer finds that the law is being broken, he or she can:

1. Give verbal or written advice.
2. Issue an improvement notice requiring the matter(s) to be remedied within a given time (this is never less than the time allowed for an appeal, 21 days).
3. Issue a prohibition notice which demands that an activity ceases until action is taken to put matters right. A prohibition notice will be issued if there is risk of serious personal injury. It can take immediate effect or on a date specified (this is known as a deferred prohibition notice).
4. Remove, destroy or make harmless anything that the officer considers to give rise to imminent danger of serious personal injury.
5. Take the person or company before the courts—this may be in addition to serving a prohibition notice. Some prosecutions are taken to publicise a particular type of breach or deal with cases of persistent and prolonged wrong-doing.

Improvement or prohibition notices may be served on the person undertaking the activity or on the person in control of the activity. An appeal against such notices can be made up to 21 days from the date of service of the notice. An appeal against an improvement notice suspends its operation until the appeal is heard, but no such automatic suspension is affected with a prohibition notice.

Offences under HASAWA

An offence is committed if anyone at work (employers, employees, self-employed people, directors, partners, etc.):

- fails to comply with the general responsibilities imposed on him/her by the Act
- fails to comply with any regulations made under the Act (see unit 13)
- obstructs officers on their inspection of the premises (EHOs or HSIs)
- fails to comply with any requirements imposed by the officer
- fails to comply with an improvement or prohibition notice
- fails to comply with a court order relating to an offence.

Penalties under HASAWA

An offence under the Health and Safety at Work Act is a criminal offence. For serious offences an unlimited fine can be imposed and/or a prison sentence of up to two years. Individuals and/or companies can be prosecuted.

In addition an employer or company can be sued for damages by anyone who is killed, injured or otherwise affected by the unsafe work activity or omission.

When an EHO or HSI inspects a premises and finds there is a risk to the health and safety of anyone using the premises, the officer will decide what action is most likely to be effective. For example if the person or people responsible for the problems appear willing to put matters right and have generally made efforts to keep the premises clean, tidy and safe, then a mild verbal caution may be given. However, if on a later visit there have been no improvements, the officer is likely to write a warning letter or, if matters have become much worse, to issue an improvement notice

The Health and Safety at Work Act (see unit 12) provides for various regulations and codes of practice to deal with specific issues.

Safety representatives and committees

The appointment and role of safety representatives and committees required under HASAWA is set out in the Safety Representatives and Safety Committees Regulations (1977). There is also a code of practice.

Where an employer recognises a trade union (or unions), the union(s) have the right to appoint safety representatives. The number of representatives will be agreed between the two parties to take account of staff numbers, the work involved, number of buildings, working hours and any special risks.

Employers must set up a safety committee if at least two safety representatives ask for this to be done. The committee will include management and staff representatives.

Where there is no recognised trade union, the employer is free to decide how best to consult and communicate with staff on health and safety issues, so long as adequate steps are taken to keep every member of staff informed. In practice even when there is no recognised trade union, most large companies have joint management-staff committees to keep a special eye on health and safety issues.

> ✱ **FOR INTEREST**
>
> The requirement to report accidents in hotel and catering establishments has actually been in force since the introduction of the Offices, Shops and Railway Premises Act (1963) (see unit 14). But it was found that many accidents were not reported, in spite of efforts by EHOs and HSIs to explain the requirements of the Act.
>
> The new regulations (RIDDOR) passed after the Health and Safety at Work Act tightened up the reporting systems.

Safety representatives

Their rights include:

- to inspect the workplace on a formal basis every three months (or more frequently by agreement), after a dangerous occurrence, notifiable accident or disease, when working conditions change or new information becomes available
- to make representations to the employer about safety matters
- to represent staff in consultations with enforcing officers (EHOs or HSIs)
- to receive information from enforcing officers which arise from their inspections
- to attend meetings of the safety committee(s).

Safety committees

Their functions include:

- to encourage co-operation between employers, management and staff on health and safety issues
- to advise on health and safety rules and policies
- to consider reports of inspections, accidents and notifiable diseases, draw attention to hazards or new information on health and safety published for instance by government, the local authority or the Health and Safety Executive, and recommend action
- to monitor the effectiveness of health and safety training.

Accidents, dangerous incidents and diseases

When there has been an accident connected with work, a dangerous health and safety problem such as an accidental explosion, or someone at work gets a disease that is a particular risk in that job, the matter must be reported to the enforcing authority (the local environmental health department for most hotel and catering establishments, otherwise the Health and Safety Executive, see unit 12). In the case of death, major injury or dangerous occurrence, the report must be made immediately (by telephone). In all cases a written report has to be made within seven days using the official form.

Most establishments keep an accident book or use their own forms to make sure the necessary information is collected when an accident occurs.

In addition to the requirements in Reporting of Injuries, Diseases and Dangerous Occurrences Regulations (1985)—RIDDOR for short—to report various diseases, food handlers suffering from or carrying certain infections must be reported to the local medical officer of health (see units 15 and 17).

> **PRACTICAL TIP**
>
> If you should be present when an accident or dangerous incident occurs there may be many urgent decisions to take, especially if you are in a position to help the injured. Nevertheless, try and remain calm and take a mental note of the details you will be asked to provide on the accident report, such as:
>
> - time of the accident/incident
> - where it occurred
> - the sequence of events.

Reportable accidents, occurrences and diseases

RIDDOR specifies what must be reported and the appropriate person in your workplace or college will have the details. Examples include:

As a result of an accident at or in connection with work
Death
Acute illness
Fracture of the skull, spine or pelvis
Fracture of any bone in the arm, wrist, leg or ankle (but not a bone in the hand or foot)
Amputation of a hand, foot, finger, thumb or toe or any part of these if the bone or joint is completely severed
Loss of eyesight, a penetrating injury to an eye or a chemical or hot metal eye burn
Burn or other injury resulting from an electric shock which requires immediate medical treatment or results in a loss of consciousness
Injuries which incapacitate a person for more than three consecutive days after the day of the accident.

Certain dangerous occurrences
The collapse, overturning of or failure of any load-bearing part of a lift, hoist or crane
Electrical short-circuit or overload which causes a fire or explosion so serious that normal work has to be stopped for more than 24 hours
The collapse or partial collapse of any part of the building or structure involving a fall of more than 5 tonnes of material.

Reportable diseases linked to work activities
Cataract (in work involving exposure to electromagnetic radiation, including radiant heat)
Occupational asthma (in work where dusts arise from processing, handling, transporting or storing barley, oats, rye, wheat or maize and meal or flour made from them).

First aid provision

The Health and Safety (First Aid) Regulations (1981) place responsibility on the employer to be able to give first aid to any staff who get injured or become ill at work. Although there is no specific requirement to make first aid provision for customers and other non-employees who may be on the premises, most establishments will take account of this need. The Regulations are accompanied by guidance notes and a code of practice.

If the nature and location of the work and the number of employees means there is a particular risk level, then trained first-aiders must be provided. Whether there is a first-aider or not, there must be an appointed person on duty to take charge of the first aid equipment and facilities and capable of summoning medical assistance if a first-aider is not available.

If there are special hazards involved in the work, a first-aider trained to deal with those hazards must be provided.

The employer must also provide a suitable number of properly-stocked first aid boxes.

YTS trainees

Trainees on the Youth Training Scheme are protected under the Health and Safety (Youth Training Scheme) Regulations (1983). In addition to the normal accident reporting procedures, the scheme organiser and Training Agency are notified and provided with a copy of the accident report.

✳ FOR INTEREST

A first-aider is someone who has gained a first aid certificate within the past three years from the St John Ambulance Association, the St Andrew's Ambulance Association or the British Red Cross Society.

The Health and Safety Executive recommends that where the hazard risk is high (many catering kitchens fall into this category) there should be a first-aider. If the hazard status is low (for example front of house, housekeeping and restaurant, where only the usual job tasks and equipment are involved) then a first-aider is recommended when the number of staff exceeds 150.

First aid boxes should be strongly-made and carry a white cross on a green background. The contents must include:

individually wrapped sterile adhesive dressings   guidance card
waterproof dressing (blue for food handlers)   antiseptics
sterile eye pad with attachment   triangular bandage
sterile covering for serious wounds   safety pins
different sizes (medium, large and extra large)
of sterile unmedicated dressings.

The number of each item will depend on the number of staff.

 **TO DO**

Have a look at the accident reporting book or forms used in two or three hotel and catering establishments of your choice. Study the layout carefully and the details requested, then have a go at designing your own form.

The Health and Safety at Work Act is concerned with general working conditions (see unit 12). There is further legislation which relates specifically to the control of hazardous substances, the working environment, the use of dangerous machines, fire precautions, safety signs, public health and the security of customers' property (see next unit).

Hazardous substances in the workplace

The Control of Substances Hazardous to Health Regulations (1988), COSHH for short, set out the essential measures that employers have to take to protect their staff from any substances used at work, or arising from work activities that can harm people's health. This includes harmful microorganisms—such as food poisoning bacteria, the bacterium which causes Legionnaires' disease and the virus which causes AIDS (see unit 45). It also includes dust, if present in substantial quantities, and cleaning agents, if they are toxic, harmful, irritant or corrosive (suppliers of such items are required by law to provide information for their safe use).

COSHH requires employers to:

- assess the risks
- introduce and maintain such measures as are necessary to prevent and control the risks
- inform and instruct staff about the risks
- train staff to take the required precautions.

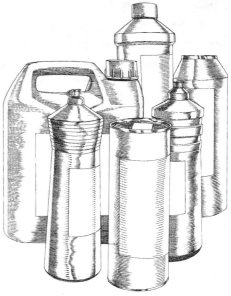

Where necessary employers must arrange for the exposure of their staff to be monitored and their health to be regularly examined. This might involve the services of a doctor or nurse, but could also include trained supervisors checking employees' skin for severe dermatitis, for example, or asking questions about breathing difficulties if the work involves substances known to cause asthma.

Failure to comply with COSHH, in addition to exposing people in the workplace to risk, is an offence and subject to penalties under the Health and Safety at Work Act.

Assessment of the risk to health arising from work is an essential requirement for all employers under the COSHH Regulations. The Health and Safety Executive recommends a systematic review of:
- what substances are present and in what form
- what harmful effects are possible
- where and how the substances are used or handled, for example:
    - is it likely that some of the substance will be breathed in
    - is it likely to be swallowed following contamination of fingers, clothing, etc.
    - is it likely to be absorbed through the skin
    - is it reasonably foreseeable that an accidental spill, leakage or discharge could occur, perhaps through a mechanical breakdown or operator error
- what harmful substances are given off during any process or work activity (for example dust or fumes)
- who could be affected, to what extent and for how long.

In all but the simplest cases, the assessment will need to be written down.

▶ ▶ ▶ TO DO

Choose an example of a substance hazardous to health which might be used in a hotel and catering establishment, for example:

- a chemical disinfectant used in the housekeeping department as a cleaning agent
- carbon dioxide gas cylinders used in the cellars for some draught beers and bulk mineral dispense systems
- oven cleaning agents used in the kitchen.

Carry out your own assessment of the risks and make some suggestions on the measures which should be taken to control the risks and protect the health of anyone handling the substance.

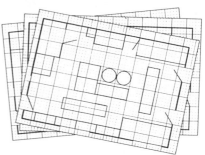

Working conditions have to meet requirements under the health and safety legislation—behind the scenes as well as in customer areas

The working environment

The Offices, Shops and Railway Premises Act (1963) provides for the health, welfare and safety of staff. Most hotel and catering establishments fall under the scope of the Act as their business is the sale to members of the public of food or drink for immediate consumption. Cafeterias or dining rooms provided for the use of office or shop staff are also covered by the Act.

- The premises, furniture, fixtures and fittings must be kept clean.
- The temperature must be maintained at no less than 16°C (61°F) and there must be an adequate supply of fresh or purified air.
- The lighting must be sufficient and suitable for the work involved.
- Corridors and stairs must be properly lit and maintained.
- There should be enough space for each person to work in and providing this does not interfere with the work, suitable seating.
- Toilet and washing facilities must be provided, with hot and cold water, soap and clean towels or hot air driers.
- Drinking water must be available.
- Where employees take their meals within the premises suitable and sufficient facilities for eating meals must be provided.
- A place to hang or store non-working clothes has to be provided. If clothing is kept in rooms where food or drink is handled, then lockers or cupboards have to be provided.
- Every dangerous part of any machine must be securely guarded.
- No person under the age of 18 may clean, lubricate or adjust any machine if doing so exposes that person to risk of injury.
- No member of staff may work machines specified as 'prescribed dangerous machines' unless he or she has been properly instructed and trained or is directly supervised or in the process of being trained.

Prescribed dangerous machines

Machines which fall into this category are specified in the Prescribed Dangerous Machines Order (1964). Of those listed the following might be found in hotel and catering establishments:

power-driven
machines of any type equipped with a circular saw blade
vegetable slicing machines
food mixing machines when used with attachments for mincing, slicing, chipping and any other cutting operation, or for crumbing
worm-type mincing machines
rotary knife bowl-type chopping machines
pie and tart making machines
dough mixers
dough brakes
wrapping and packing machines

power-driven or manual
circular knife slicing machines
potato chipping machines
guillotine machines (e.g. for paper cutting)

Other potentially dangerous machines

rotary bowl mixers
band saws
walk-in cold rooms and deep freezer stores
microwave ovens
floor cleaning and polishing machines
spirit or gas cookers used in restaurants to cook, flame or re-heat food
fans and moving parts of motors and compressors
lifts, hoists and dummy waiters
escalators
refuse compactors
(See units 28, 30, 37, 41 and 42.)

15 THE LAW

Fire safety

The law protects the occupants of most public buildings against the dangers of fire (see also units 18 to 22). In some cases the protection is indirect, for example a licence to sell alcohol will not be given to an establishment where the fire safety measures are poor or non-existent, planning permission will not be given to a new building unless adequate fire exits are provided and safe materials used in its construction.

The Fire Precautions Act (1971) now covers all but the smallest hotels, motels, inns and boarding houses, and non-residential establishments such as restaurants, pubs, fish and chip shops and cafés.

Under the Act it is unlawful for the owners or occupiers of buildings used by the public to carry on in business unless they hold a fire certificate issued by the local fire authority and meet all the requirements. This places a limit on the number of people who can be on the premises at one time and covers the provision of:

- fire warning systems, including notices to guests and staff (in more than one language if necessary)
- fire fighting equipment
- escape routes
- regular training for staff in fire procedures.

Safety signs

All safety signs must meet certain requirements, even if they have been put up to warn people of a specific but short-term hazard, for example wet paint. Hand-made signs using any colour paint which comes to hand and a convenient left-over piece of board should not be used.

Under the Safety Signs Regulations (1980) all safety signs must comply with British Standard 5378. This specifies four categories of sign, each with its own shape and colour. The categories are the same in all EC countries.

Prohibition a red outline circle on a white background with a red cross bar
Warning a black outline triangle with a solid yellow centre
Safe condition a solid green rectangle or square with rounded corners
Mandatory a solid blue circle

Within the circle, triangle, rectangle or square a symbol is inserted to indicate the nature of the hazard. These symbols are also specified in BS 5378.

Fire safety signs use the same framework of colours and design.

Premises not covered by the Fire Precautions Act include:

- establishments where all the bedrooms are on the ground and/or first floor and provide beds for fewer than six people (guests and/or staff)
- small establishments in which not more than ten people are working at any one time other than on the ground floor and the total number of employees in the building at any one time is not more than 20.

Additional text can be used with safety signs, if required. The text is displayed in an oblong or square box of the same colour as the sign, with the letters in white against backgrounds of red, green or blue, or in black against a yellow background. Text must always be kept apart from the symbol and should never interfere with it

Prohibition	Warning	Safe condition	Mandatory
Don't do	Risk of danger	The safe way	Must do

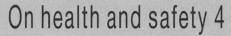
Protecting the public health

Hoteliers and others offering sleeping accommodation to the public must not let a room which is known to have been occupied by someone suffering from a notifiable infectious disease until the room and its contents have been disinfected. The local authority medical officer of health or other registered medical practitioner must issue a clearance certificate before the room can be let to another person.

Anyone suffering from a notifiable infectious disease is committing an offence and can be fined if he or she is aware of carrying the disease and exposes other people to the risk of infection by:

- his or her presence or conduct in any public place (this includes places of entertainment or assembly, hotels, shops, even the street)
- engaging in or carrying on any work activity which might risk spreading the disease.

> In England and Wales the provisions are contained in the Public Health (Control of Disease) Act (1984) and the Public Health (Infectious Diseases) Regulations (1988). The notifiable diseases listed include: measles, mumps, malaria, meningitis, viral hepatitis, whooping cough, cholera, plague, relapsing fever, smallpox, typhus, acute encephalitis, acute poliomyelitis, anthrax, diphtheria, dysentery (amoebic or bacillary), leprosy, leptospirosis, meningococcal septicaemia (without meningitis), paratyphoid fever, rubella, scarlet fever, tuberculosis, typhoid fever, and viral haemorrhagic fever.
>
> In Scotland the provisions are contained in the Public Health (Infectious Disease) Regulations (Scotland) (1932/68), Public Health Infectious Diseases (Notification) (Scotland) Act (1889), Food and Drugs (Scotland) Act (1956) and Public Health (Scotland) Act (1897).

Protecting customers' property

Under the Hotel Proprietors Act (1956) the proprietors of any establishments offering sleeping accommodation are responsible for the reception and safe-keeping of all reasonable items of luggage belonging to guests who have booked into the hotel, inn or motel for one night or more.

- The proprietor is *fully liable* if the loss or damage to the guest's property is caused solely by the negligence or wilful act of the proprietor or the staff. If the goods have been entrusted to the hotel for safe-keeping, or such a request was made and refused, then the guest is also entitled to full compensation for loss or damage.
- If the loss or damage is caused by an act of God or the Queen's enemies or total negligence on the part of the guest, then the proprietor incurs *no liability*.
- *Liability is limited* if the loss or damage does not exactly fit into either of the above categories and the notice required by the Act is prominently displayed in reception or near the main entrance to the building. This notice limits liability to £50 for any one article and a total of £100 for any one guest.

Cars parked on the proprietor's property without payment of a parking fee, property left in guest's cars, horses and other types of animal are not regarded as reasonable items of luggage.

The limits to liability do not extend to the property of customers of the restaurant or bar, for example, unless they have booked overnight accommodation. They also do not apply to guesthouses, private hotels and leisure centres, for example, which only accept guests by prior contract and so do not come within the legal definition of a hotel. The normal laws of contract and negligence apply in these cases.

▶ ▶ ▶ **TO DO**

Visit a variety of establishments, including if possible a hotel, a pub or restaurant and a theatre or shop where coats and similar personal property can be left for safe-keeping. Explain your interest and ask the management if you can take a photograph of the notices which are displayed limiting the proprietor or company's liability for customers' property, or copy down the wording. Discuss with your supervisor or tutor examples of where the owners of the establishments you visited would be liable for the property, in spite of the notices limiting or disclaiming liability.

The laws on food hygiene and handling cover all aspects of food and drink preparation and service in hotel and catering establishments, including transportation, storage, packing, wrapping, displaying and labelling. The legislation covers any food and drink intended for sale or sold for human consumption on any premises in or from which a food business is carried out, whether for a profit or not—so, for example, clubs, schools, hospitals and welfare catering are included. It also includes anything likely to be used in the preparation of food and drink.

General guidelines to the legislation, Part I

Offences

1. It is an offence to sell or offer for sale any food or drink that is unfit for human consumption or is likely to make people ill. A person who consigns such food to someone else to sell would also be committing an offence.
2. It is an offence to sell any food or drink that is not of the nature, substance or quality demanded by the purchaser, for example if the whisky or gin is watered down, there is a piece of broken china in the soup, pork claiming to be veal is served, or frozen vegetables are served as 'fresh'.
3. It is an offence to give a label to food or drink which is intended to mislead or falsely describes the item.

Responsibility

4. Everyone who handles food and/or drink has some responsibility and can be charged for an offence. Anyone not actually handling food and drink but with a management or supervisory responsibility for others who do, also has a responsibility and can be charged for an offence. This includes the owners of the business.

Premises and facilities

5. There must be a suitable supply of clean and wholesome water to the premises.
6. Any room or area in which food and/or drink is stored or handled must be clean, properly maintained and in such good order that it can be cleaned without the need for extensive effort and kept free from vermin. It must also be suitably lit and have a suitable and sufficient means of ventilation (unless it is, for example, a cold room).
7. Food rooms must not be used as a sleeping place.
8. The toilets must be well lit and ventilated and kept in a state of thorough cleanliness, free from any foreign matter. (The term toilet refers to any room or area containing a sanitary convenience such as a WC or urinal, which is situated in the premises of a food business, or used regularly by staff who handle food or drink.)
9. Toilets must be positioned so that no offensive odours can penetrate into any room in which food or drink is handled. This usually means there must be an intervening ventilated space between the toilet and any food room.
10. The toilet areas must never be used to store any food or drink item, even if it is in a sealed container, nor equipment or utensils used in the preparation or service of food or drink, nor cleaning materials.
11. Food and drink must not be handled or stored in any room which communicates directly with a toilet or sleeping place, unless it is in a sealed container or fully protected from contamination by a suitable wrapping.

✳ FOR INTEREST

The Food and Environment Protection Act (1985) provides the government with powers to prevent contaminated food being sold or served to the public, for example in the event of a major chemical accident. Activities which could be banned include the preparation of food by caterers.

✳ FOR INTEREST

There are restrictions on the preparation or packing of food on domestic premises, so it would be illegal, for example, to prepare pub food in the landlord's private kitchen. Where a food business is being carried on from domestic premises, as would be the case in a small guesthouse, for example, these restrictions do not apply.

12. There must be a notice in the toilets to remind those who have used them to wash their hands.

13. Wash hand basins must be kept clean and in good working order. A nail brush, supply of soap or suitable detergent and hand-drying facilities must be provided at each wash hand basin.

14. Wash hand basins are for maintaining personal cleanliness. They must never be used for washing or storing food or equipment.

15. Wash hand basins should be provided in the toilets and in areas where food and drink is handled, conveniently placed to encourage staff to use them. They should have hot and cold running water (or hot water maintained at a suitable temperature). In premises where only sealed, packed or securely covered food is handled a cold water supply at wash hand basins is sufficient.

16. There must be suitable and sufficient sinks or other facilities to wash food and equipment, with a supply of hot and cold water (or hot water maintained at a suitable temperature). For sinks which are used for washing fish, vegetables or fruit only, a supply of cold water is sufficient.

17. Outlets to the drainage system from sinks, waste disposal units, floor gullies, drainage channels etc. must be fitted with a water seal.

Food and drink storage and handling

18. Food and drink intended for sale must be kept apart from any food or drink which is unfit for human consumption. This means the premises must have adequate space and be designed so there are separate areas for storing or dealing with waste and rubbish.

19. Waste or refuse should not be allowed to remain in rooms where food is stored or handled for any longer than necessary.

20. Food must not be kept at temperatures which encourage bacteria to multiply.

21. Cooked food must not be stored or prepared in such a way that it comes into contact with raw food (as the raw food is likely to contaminate the cooked food).

22. Cleaning materials must not be stored where they can come into contact with food or drink intended for consumption.

23. In open areas, such as the delivery bay, food and drink items must not be placed less than half a metre (18 inches) from the ground unless they are in sealed containers.

24. Food displayed for sale, for example in self-service counters, must be kept covered or effectively screened from possible sources of contamination (open displays of food on buffet tables and dessert trolleys for example, can present a likely source of danger).

25. Materials used for wrapping or containing food must be clean and made of a substance which will not contaminate the food. Printed materials such as newspapers, must not come into contact with food—but printed materials can be used to wrap uncooked vegetables.

26. No live animal must be allowed to come into contact with any food or drink intended for human consumption, and animal food must not be stored in any food room unless it is in its own sealed container.

27. Working surfaces, cooking equipment and utensils, storage containers, service equipment and any other items which come in contact with the food and drink must be kept clean and free from contamination. These items must be made of a material that will not absorb matter—so wooden chopping boards, for instance, are unsuitable. They should also be made in such a way and kept in such a condition that they can be thoroughly cleaned.

▶ ▶ ▶   TO DO

Choose two practices covered in the legislation on food and drink hygiene (summarised in this and the next unit) which you feel staff may not know enough about or which might get overlooked in the day to day pressures of a busy kitchen, such as:

- requirements to report certain infections
- covering cuts and open sores
- use of wash hand basins
- storage of cleaning materials

and make a poster for each which would help staff to keep within the law and generally encourage good practice.

General guidelines to the legislation, Part II

Food handlers

28. All those handling food must keep the parts of their body and their clothes which can come into contact with food and drink clean. Any parts of the body or clothing the hands are likely to touch must also be kept clean.

29. Cuts, open sores and wounds must be kept covered with a waterproof dressing. (Suitable first aid material including bandages, dressings and antiseptic must be provided at the workplace.)

30. Smoking, spitting or taking snuff in a room or area where uncovered food and/or drink is handled is forbidden.

31. Clean and washable overclothing must be worn. This does not apply to someone who only handles raw vegetables, for example a kitchen assistant, nor to anyone handling only alcohol or soft drinks, for example barstaff, nor to food serving staff—provided the person takes care not to let any food or drink come into contact with his or her clothing. Butchers, porters or anyone else who carries uncovered raw meat in such a way that it might come into contact with their neck or hair must also wear clean and washable neck and head covering. Outdoor clothing and footwear must be kept in the locker, cupboard or changing room provided. Sufficient clean overclothing must be available to enable staff to change as and when necessary.

32. No one must handle food while suffering from or carrying typhoid, paratyphoid, other salmonella infections, amoebic dysentery, bacillary dysentery or any staphylococcal infection likely to cause food poisoning such as septic cuts, boils, spots, burns, a throat or nasal infection. The illness must be reported immediately to the person in charge of the business and that person must notify the local medical officer of health at once. Anyone infected in this way must not return to handling food until cleared by a doctor as fit to do so.

▶ ▶ ▶ TO DO

With the help of your tutor or supervisor or the librarian at your local public library, find out as much as you can about a recent incident where a hotel or catering establishment in your area has been in difficulty under the food hygiene legislation. Back copies of local and trade papers and magazines will be a useful source of information. What was the alleged offence? What defence was offered by the management/staff of the establishment? What was the outcome? What action did the business take to put matters right? What affect on the business did the publicity seem to have?

The legislation

In England and Wales

The Food Act (1984) brought together a large amount of legislation concerning the preparation and sale of food. It gives government ministers the power to make regulations regarding the composition, labelling and description of food and to secure hygienic conditions in connection with the sale, importation, preparation, transport, storage, packing, wrapping, exposure for sale, service or delivery of food for human consumption. Regulations made include the:

- Food Hygiene (General) Regulations (1970)
- Food Hygiene (Markets, Stalls and Delivery Vehicles) Regulations (1966)
- Food Labelling Regulations (1984)
- Materials and Articles in Contact with Food Regulations (1987)
- Bread and Flour Regulations (1984).

The Food Act gives local authorities and their enforcing officers (EHOs) various powers to control food premises and the supply of food and drink intended for human consumption (or any substance used in their preparation). These include:

- to enter the premises at any reasonable hour to investigate possible contraventions
- to purchase or take samples (of food or drink)
- to examine the food or drink and if it appears unfit for human consumption to remove it in order to have it dealt with by a Justice of the Peace
- to examine vehicles or containers thought to be holding food or drink
- to apply for a court order to disqualify a person who has broken the hygiene regulations from using the offending premises as catering premises for up to two years
- to apply to a magistrate's court for the closure of a food business (if there is imminent risk of danger to health an emergency order will be made).

A person guilty of an offence is liable, on summary conviction, to a fine and, on indictment, to a fine and/or prison sentence of up to two years.

In Scotland

- Premises may be closed under the Control of Food Premises (Scotland) Act (1977).
- The handling, preparation and offering for sale of food is controlled under the Food and Drugs (Scotland) Act (1956).
- The composition and labelling of food is controlled under the Food Labelling (Scotland) Regulations (1984).
- Provision for food hygiene controls is made in the Food Hygiene (Scotland) Regulations (1959/78).

Changes to the food hygiene laws were announced in July 1989 in a government white paper *Food Safety—Protecting the Consumer*.

- The Food Act (1984) and comparable Scottish legislation will be replaced with a new act covering England, Wales and Scotland, with regulations to extend it to Northern Ireland. The food hygiene regulations will be tightened up.
- Enforcing officers (EHOs) will be given stronger powers to seize unfit food, to condemn whole batches of food and to close down catering premises more quickly.
- All hotels, restaurants and other catering establishments will have to be registered with the local authority.
- Food irradiation and other technical developments in food processing and catering will be dealt with in the new legislative framework.
- Training of food handlers may be made compulsory.
- 'Best before' and 'sell by' labels on perishable foods will be phased out and replaced with a 'use by' date.

Fires cause damage to property, loss of business, injury and death. In hotel, catering, leisure and tourism establishments fire is a particularly serious hazard.

- Many of the guests, residents, visitors and other occupants will be unfamiliar with the building's layout.
- In accommodation establishments there will be people sleeping in the building at times when no-one may be about to sound the alarm if a fire starts.
- It is difficult in any building which is open to the public to control people's behaviour and some customers and staff will be less careful than they would be in their own home.

The Fire Precautions Act (1971) sets down the regulations for fire safety in the industry (see unit 15). These include how to prevent fire from breaking out, what to do in the event of a fire and staff training. Failure to comply with the regulations can cost thousands of pounds in fines and legal costs.

How to prevent fire

- Report anyone behaving suspiciously, for example 'guests' in strictly staff-only areas.
- Fire escape routes should be checked daily, so should vacant rooms. Conference, meeting and exhibition rooms should also be carefully checked after they have been used.
- Ashtrays should be provided in sufficient numbers in all rooms and areas where people might smoke. Paper plates or other items made of flammable material should never be used as make-shift ashtrays. Ashtrays in public areas should be regularly emptied, and special care should be taken if they are the type that passers-by throw in empty packets and other paper wrappings.
- Ashtrays should always be emptied into metal bins with hinged tops, never into any container which might melt or go up in flames, and never placed with other rubbish such as paper which might get set alight. Metal bins are best for any rubbish which might catch fire as the bin itself will not ignite, or melt (as plastic would) spilling the burning contents on to the floor.
- Waste should be stored outside the building as far as possible.
- All cleaning rags, linen, rubbish, chemicals and any flammable items must be carefully stored in the correct places.
- Guards should be placed in front of open fires if there is no-one to keep a watchful eye on the fire.
- Electric bar fires and fan heaters should be kept away from furniture and furnishings. Staff and guests should be discouraged from using multi-point adaptors. Plugs should be removed from sockets when the appliances are not in use. The manufacturer's instructions should be carefully followed for equipment such as radio alarms and video recorders which are left plugged in all the time.
- Electrical wiring and other electrical installations should be inspected and tested by a qualified electrician regularly and at least every five years. All electrical equipment should be regularly checked to ensure it is in working order. Staff should report any faults or potential hazards immediately so they can be put right by qualified personnel.
- Fire fighting equipment should be inspected regularly to ensure that all items are in place and working correctly. Smoke-stop doors should be checked daily, fire alarms weekly if possible and certainly every three months. Hose

May 28, 1981: firemen hosing down the remains of Heston service station restaurant. The fire started in a toilet, after midnight

✳ FOR INTEREST

- There are nearly 2000 fires each year in hotels, guesthouses and similar establishments in Britain. In 1986 fires in hotels resulted in four deaths and 100 casualties.
- About one-third of these fires were caused by electrical faults and a similar proportion by smoking.
- Fires are particularly likely to start in bedrooms (often due to smoking), in public rooms such as restaurants or lounges and in kitchens.
- Fire can also break out in unoccupied rooms, such as storerooms and conference rooms, where some time may pass before it is discovered.
- Most hotel fires involving death or injury occur between midnight and five o'clock in the morning when people are in bed asleep, and evacuation of the building can take longer.

Outside contractors carrying out work in the building should be supervised to ensure they don't:

- block escape routes with equipment
- leave paint, gas cylinders or other flammable items where they are a potential hazard
- use blow lamps or other equipment involving high temperatures without warning the management in advance.

reels should be checked every three months and emergency lighting every six months. Extinguishers should be examined annually by an expert (the inspection date will be written on a label on the equipment).

- Doors, including internal doors, and windows should be closed where possible to stop the spread of fire.
- Fire doors should be kept closed and free from obstructions. They should not be bolted or locked (unless a means of opening the door in an emergency is provided, such as a key in a glass-covered box by the door).
- Fire exits must be clearly marked and fully accessible. Fire alarm points, fire fighting equipment, exit notices, direction signs and escape routes must be lit at times when there is not sufficient natural light available. They should be connected to a back-up electricity supply in case the main circuit is cut off when a fire breaks out.

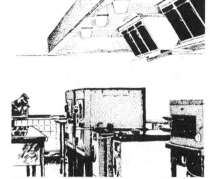

Kitchen staff should take special precautions to prevent fires by:

- taking care not to overheat the oil or fat when shallow or deep frying
- never placing wet food into hot oil or fat
- never leaving deep fat fryers or frying pans unattended while they are turned on or left over a heat source
- not overfilling pans, roasting and baking trays
- removing any build-up of grease in filters, extraction hoods or on cooking equipment (often this job will be left to specialists, perhaps on a contract basis)
- not leaving clothes to dry over cooking equipment.

✳ FOR INTEREST

Fire safety should be one of the most important considerations when new hotel and catering establishments are planned, existing places renovated or new equipment, furnishing and fittings purchased.

- Buying fire-retardant materials and fabrics and choosing furniture which has no crevices to hide dropped cigarettes. New upholstered furniture must comply with the Upholstered Furniture (Safety) Regulations (1980).
- Installing up-to-date emergency lighting. (Important improvements have been made to emergency lighting systems in recent years.)
- Installing smoke detectors. (These may soon be made compulsory.)
- Providing ashtrays which are large enough to avoid overflowing and have no rim at all or are designed so that if cigarettes do overbalance they will fall into the centre, not on to the table or other surrounding surface.
- Providing eye-catching fire notices in several languages.
- Adapting fire alarm systems in bedrooms which might be let to the hard of hearing. For example providing jack-in plugs so that bed-frame vibrators and

stroboscopic lamp devices can be connected to ensure that even profoundly deaf people will become aware of the fire alarm system being activated—whether they are awake or asleep.

- Fastening fire extinguishers to the wall on brackets to discourage staff using them to prop open doors.
- Fitting fire doors in busy corridors with electromagnetic door stops so they are normally held open, and will close automatically in the event of a fire. This will discourage people from wedging such doors open because it is awkward to push trolleys through them, for example.
- Connecting fire exit doors to an electronic system which will alert a security person if any door is opened (see unit 23).
- Installing automatic fire detection and extinguishing systems. An extensive choice is available to meet most needs, for example dry power extinguishers in hoods and ducts in kitchens to provide round-the-clock protection over cooking areas, equipment to shut down fuel supplies, turning off air-conditioning systems (these can fan the flames) and lifts (returning them to the ground floor).

➧ ➧ ➧ TO DO

Obtain a copy of the fire procedure used at your place of work or at an establishment of your choice. Read through it carefully and make sure you understand it. With permission, walk around the building and take note of the position of the fire alarms, fire exits, fire doors, smoke detectors and different types of fire fighting equipment. Design a notice and map which would help anyone not familiar with the layout of the building to know what to do in the event of a fire. You may wish to concentrate on a particular part of the building such as the leisure centre, or a group of guest/staff bedrooms. If some of the people the notice is intended to help have difficulty understanding English repeat the instructions in a language they will understand (with the help of colleagues or your tutor/supervisor if necessary).

19 FIRE

It is important for everyone to know what to do if a fire breaks out in a building they work or live in, are staying in for a night or two, or just spending a few hours in. In buildings which are open to the public, management and staff have an extra responsibility towards the safety of others who are less familiar with the building, its layout and fire procedures.

- If staff are familiar with the escape routes and exits they are in a better position to help others reach safety.
- When staff know immediately what action to take if they hear the fire alarm or are the first to discover a fire, they can reduce the damage to the building and help reduce the risk of personal injury.

The Fire Precautions Act (see units 15 and 18) requires that staff training in hotels and similar establishments should meet certain minimum standards.

1. All staff should receive their own copy of the procedures to be taken in the event of a fire. For staff who do not have a good grasp of written English, these instructions should be in a language they will easily understand.
2. Each new member of staff should have in the first month of employment two periods of at least 30 minutes of verbal instruction by a competent person.
3. All staff should have at least one 30 minutes' period of verbal instruction every six months.
4. Staff who are sometimes or regularly on night duties should have verbal instruction every three months.
5. Exercises for all staff should take place at least every six months. These can be combined with the period of verbal instruction.
6. In small premises where not more than four staff are available the exercise can take the form of a walk through the premises to check fire and escape routes, emergency exits, fire doors, the position of fire alarms, fire fighting equipment and so on.

STAFF FIRE INSTRUCTIONS

IF YOU DISCOVER A FIRE

1. Activate the nearest "Break Glass Point"
2. Call the switchboard, 222 and inform the operator of the location of the fire.
3. Pick up one of the "Back of House" fire telephones and inform the operator of the location of the fire.
   Attack the fire if possible with the appliances provided but without taking personal risks.

FIRE ALARMS

1. The ALERT ALARM sounds in the effected area — prepare to evacuate.
2. The EVACUATE ALARM is a continuous sounding of the alarm. On hearing this all persons will leave the building and proceed to the Assembly Point, Christ Church, corner of Down Street and Brick Street. Group into Departments for Roll Call.

■ USE NEAREST AVAILABLE EXIT

■ DO NOT USE LIFTS

■ DO NOT STOP TO COLLECT PERSONAL BELONGINGS

■ DO NOT RE-ENTER THE BUILDING

‼ REMEMBER

While it may seem fun during a fire exercise to shoot off an extinguisher in the car park or garden, if you ever have to use one to fight a real fire it is vital you are well prepared.

- When the extinguishing medium hits a real fire it may well cause alarming volumes of smoke and fumes to be given off.
- The extinguisher will seem very noisy when it is used in a confined space.
- Extinguishers operate for between 30 seconds and two minutes so you will have to use them effectively every moment of this time to have a chance of putting the fire out.

7. In larger premises the exercise should include a simulated evacuation drill and the whole premises should be checked as if a real emergency was taking place.
8. One person will be responsible for organising staff training in premises, with the help in large establishments of other nominated people.
9. Detailed records must be kept of training sessions and fire practices held.

Since it is not possible to evacuate the guests from the building during fire exercises, nor to involve them in any way, it is important that they should be disturbed as little as possible. They should be warned that a fire drill is going to take place so that they are not alarmed. The drill will usually be started by a pre-determined signal, not the full operation of the fire alarm.

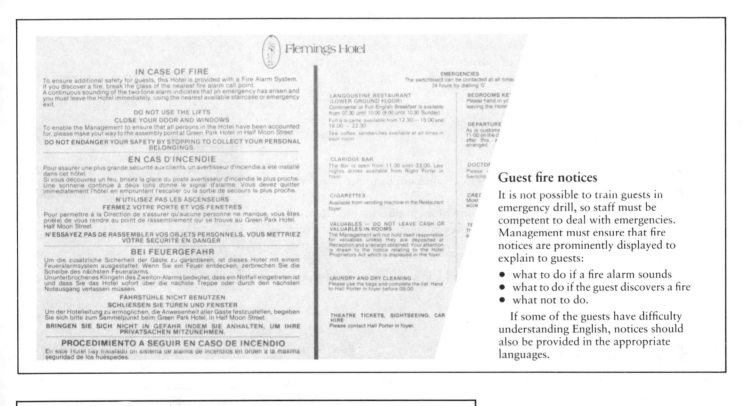

Guest fire notices

It is not possible to train guests in emergency drill, so staff must be competent to deal with emergencies. Management must ensure that fire notices are prominently displayed to explain to guests:

- what to do if a fire alarm sounds
- what to do if the guest discovers a fire
- what not to do.

If some of the guests have difficulty understanding English, notices should also be provided in the appropriate languages.

▶ ▶ ▶ TO DO

Brush up on your last fire instruction by asking yourself the following questions. Check your answers with your supervisor or tutor and note any information you have not got correct. It may be best to write your answers down so you can check them at a convenient time.

1. What would be the three most likely causes of a fire in your establishment?
2. Which items in your work area are particularly flammable?
3. If you discover a fire, what action do you take to alert (a) the fire brigade, (b) the occupants of the building and (c) someone in authority?

4. Where are the exit routes? If you work, study or live in a large building include the areas you might be in.
5. Where is your assembly point if you have to evacuate the building?
6. Who is responsible for checking the names of everyone who should have evacuated the building?
7. What fire fighting equipment is available? Include extinguishers available for fighting particular types of fire.
8. How are the different types of fire fighting equipment operated?
9. When is it safe for you to attempt to fight a fire?

20 FIRE

In the event of a fire, correct and prompt action can save lives and property. Staff should never tackle a fire if doing so puts their own life in danger. However, small localised fires can sometimes be put out by using the fire fighting equipment available. All staff should know where the fire fighting equipment is kept and how to use it.

How fire starts

A fire results when there is a combination of:

- *fuel*—this may be paper, wood, cooking oils, fabric or any other flammable object
- *heat*—this may originate from faulty electrical equipment or a cigarette end, or may be direct heat from a gas burner or electrical element in the kitchen
- *air*—air contains oxygen which enables the fire to burn.

How fire spreads

Open doors and windows will encourage a fire to burn faster by increasing the oxygen supply and fanning the flames. This is why it is important to close windows and doors immediately a fire breaks out.

As the fire develops smoke and gases, many of them poisonous, are produced. These are lighter than air and rise up until they encounter an obstacle such as a ceiling, where they spread out and pass horizontally through any openings into corridors and from one storey to the next.

Open doors, staircases and lift shafts will all allow the passage of smoke and gases.

How fires are detected

The longer the fire has to take hold, the more difficult it is to put out so the earliest possible detection of fires is of the greatest importance. Sophisticated fire detecting equipment has been developed to catch fires quickly and to safeguard the building and its occupants at night time when few people are about. Systems include:

- Smoke detectors which respond to the high concentrations of very small particles that scarcely anything other than a fire creates. They are suitable for bedrooms, general storage rooms, stairwells, corridors, public rooms and lift shafts. Special versions are available for the ducts in air-conditioning and heating systems (as these will rapidly circulate toxic fumes throughout a building).
- Flame detectors which respond to the radiation given off by a flame. They are only suitable for areas where any fire is likely to involve a flame.
- Heat detectors which respond to temperatures above a pre-set level, or which rise rapidly. These are suitable in boiler rooms, kitchens, laundries and similar areas where the working temperatures are often quite high.
- Manual alarms strategically located so that anyone in the building can strike one very quickly if a fire is observed.

!! **REMEMBER**

You should never ignore a fire alarm because you think it is a false one or a test you have not been told about. One day it may be a real fire which could harm you and everyone else in the building and even cause deaths unless prompt action is taken.

Fire doors will prevent smoke and gases from spreading and contain the fire for long enough to allow people to escape. Bedroom doors may also be made of fire-resistant material which will confine the fire to one room for up to 30 minutes

◆ ◆ ◆ **TO DO**

Have a close look at two different buildings which are near you and used as a department store, hotel or entertainment centre. Choose a modern one, built in the last five years or so and an older one, built around 75 years or more ago. Note the precautions taken in each to prevent fire spreading, for example partitions and fire doors to close off open stairwells in the older building. Note also the fire detection systems in use and any automatic fire fighting equipment. You may be able to arrange to be shown these—especially if you can organise the visit in advance and go with a group of colleagues who share your interest.

Smoke and poisonous gases cause more deaths than the actual fire by suffocating anyone who is unable to escape. Smoke will also prevent people from recognising an escape route

How a fire is put out

A fire will go out if the burning material is removed or cooled down, or if the supply of air (and therefore oxygen) is cut off.

Fire fighting equipment acts by:

* cooling down the burning materials—water hoses and sprinklers do this
* shutting off the supply of air—many fire extinguishers do this by smothering the fire in a foam, powder or gas (for example, carbon dioxide). Fire blankets and fire buckets filled with sand work on the same principle.

Fire extinguishers Extinguishers have a limited capacity, but have the advantage of being easily carried to the fire and quickly put to work. Different types of extinguisher are designed to fight different types of fires so it is important to use the correct kind.

Water—used for extinguishing paper, wood, textile and fabric-fuelled fires. The water cools down the burning item and will reduce the supply of oxygen to the fire when it is used in quantity.

Foam—used for flammable liquids such as oil, fats, paints, gas and petrol. May be used instead of water extinguishers on small surface fires. The mass of tiny bubbles cover the burning material cooling it down and shutting off the oxygen supply.

Carbon dioxide—used for flammable gases, liquids and fires involving electricity. The carbon dioxide dilutes the oxygen content of the air at the fire.

Dry powder—used for flammable liquids and gases and fires involving electricity. Can be used instead of water extinguishers on small surface fires. A special dry powder extinguisher is available for fires involving burning metals.

Halon—used for flammable liquids and gases and fires involving electricity. The (heavy) halon lies on top of the burning surface so excluding oxygen from the fire. However halon also gives off toxic fumes so halon extinguishers should not be used in confined spaces where people are present. They are suitable for outdoor use and for automatic fire fighting systems in rooms with computers, for example, where other types of extinguishing medium would cause even worse damage than the fire.

The various types of extinguisher use a colour coding so they are easily recognisable. British Standard 5423 recommends that all extinguishers should be red with an additional colour code to indicate the extinguishing medium:

water—red   *carbon dioxide*—black
foam—cream   *halon*—green
dry powder—blue

Many extinguishers are still in use where the appropriate colour is the predominant colour—the whole cylinder is black or green, for example.

FIRE

!! REMEMBER

Always use the correct type of extinguisher for the type of fire you are attempting to put out.

- Never use a water (red) extinguisher on electrical, petrol, oil or fat fires. Burning electrical equipment, if it is still connected to the electricity supply (that is 'live') will conduct electricity through the water causing shock to anyone who comes into contact with it. Fat, oil or petrol will float on top of the water from the extinguisher, causing the fire to spread further.
- Never use foam extinguishers (cream) on fires involving electricity. The foam will conduct the electricity.
- Never use carbon dioxide (black) extinguishers in a confined space because they contain harmful fumes.
- Never use halon (green) extinguishers indoors or on fires involving wood, cardboard, paper or textiles. ·

?? HOW TO

Use a fire extinguisher

1. Select correct type of extinguisher (cylinder).
2. Release cylinder from wall bracket.
3. Position at a safe distance from fire.
4. Pull out pin.
5. Free hose.
6. Squeeze lever.

Red, black, blue or green extinguishers
7a. Aim at base of fire.

Cream extinguishers
7b. Spread over fire area.

Stand firmly on both feet because the force at which the contents of the cylinder empties is quite strong, especially for carbon dioxide extinguishers.

Fire blankets   These are kept rolled up in red cylinders, equipped with a quick release tape. Fire blankets are usually made partly of non-flammable fibreglass and are particularly useful for putting out burning fat or oil, where the use of an extinguisher might cause the fat or oil to splash and spread.

Large fire blankets are used primarily to wrap around people whose clothes have caught alight—a hazard particularly in kitchens.

The blanket works by smothering the flames, cutting off the supply of air to the fire.

?? HOW TO

Use a fire blanket

1. Lift the blanket high with both hands, arms extended upwards. This action will protect the user's body.
2. Taking care, drop the blanket over the flames in a movement away from the body.
3. If a person's clothes are on fire, wrap the blanket around the burning area, keeping the victim's nose and mouth open to the air so that he or she can still breathe.
4. Take care that the blanket does not flap, thus fanning the flames.

Sand   Some establishments still provide sand buckets as a means of extinguishing fires. The buckets are usually red and are hung on hooks from the wall. The contents are thrown on to the flames and are useful only on very small fires.

Water hoses   Large hose reels connected to a water supply are strategically placed throughout the building.

Water hoses are very effective once they have been brought into operation as they give a limitless supply of water. However a disadvantage is that the hoses are heavy and difficult to unwind quickly.

PRACTICAL TIP

It is tempting to put rubbish into sand buckets and some customers will stub their cigarettes out in them. If flammable items are found in the sand it should not be used. This is just one of the reasons why fire equipment should be checked regularly by staff.

Sprinklers Some alarms are linked to sprinklers which spray water, as well as setting off the alarm, to hold back the fire until the fire brigade arrives.

Hydrant systems These are direct mains water outlets for fire brigade hoses (which require massive amounts of water). Usually they are installed in the street, but large hotels and high buildings may be required to install their own.

> ▶ ▶ ▶   **TO DO**
>
> At your place of work or study, identify what methods of fire fighting equipment are used. Draw up a chart showing what equipment should be used for:
> (a) fires involving solid materials such as wood, fabric, cardboard, paper, or furniture or rubbish which contains such materials
> (b) fires involving flammable liquids and gases such as oils, fats, paint and petrol
> (c) fires involving electrical installations or equipment.

If there is a fire on the premises, staff have a duty to look after their own safety as well as that of their colleagues and customers. Correct and swift action on discovering a fire can mean the difference between life and death. It is vital therefore that all staff know what they have to do if a fire breaks out.

Each establishment will have its procedure and regular fire instruction and exercises will have been held to train staff. They should know, for instance, where the fire fighting equipment is kept, where the nearest escape routes and exits are, and where their assembly point is outside. This is particularly important in larger establishments which may also be several storeys high.

An orderly evacuation of a building requires team work, with each member of staff calmly, quietly and quickly doing their bit. The main aim is to get everyone out of the building—alive. However valuable property and buildings are, they come second after saving human lives.

At no time should staff put their own lives at risk. Leave the heroics to the fire brigade.

No single person will be responsible for all the procedures mentioned in this unit. The idea is that staff should concentrate on their own particular responsibilities and carry out these as calmly and efficiently as possible. Senior members of staff will be in charge of co-ordinating the overall evacuation. A fire routine notice must by law be displayed in all staff areas explaining what to do in the event of a fire.

If you discover a fire first
1. Remain calm.
2. Walk, don't run.
3. Raise the alarm by operating the nearest fire alarm.
4. Call for help using the procedure laid down by the establishment.
5. Attack the fire with the equipment provided but only if this will not put you in personal danger.
6. Leave the building with the guests by the nearest safe route and exit, helping those who need it. But do not risk your own life.

If you hear the fire alarm
1. Remain calm.
2. Walk, don't run.
3. Someone will be responsible for informing the switchboard or reception about the fire. Larger establishments have a direct emergency line to the switchboard and sometimes to the fire brigade, which staff should be aware of. Reception, switchboard or a manager in charge at the time will then call the fire brigade by dialling 999.
4. Rouse the guests and make sure they know there is a fire.
5. Leave the premises with the guests by the nearest safe route and exit, giving special help to those in need. But do not risk your own life in doing so.
6. Report to the person in charge at the assembly point outside.

Before leaving the building
The following precautions should be taken only if they do not endanger life. It is important to remain calm when making these split-second decisions.

1. Switch off all electrical and gas appliances.
2. Close all windows and the doors which will not be used during the evacuation.
3. Close doors after everyone has passed through.

> ▶ ▶ ▶ **TO DO**
>
> Discuss the following incident with a group of your colleagues.
>
> *Derek Wisebanker has used a portable electric element which he always carries with him on sales trips, to make a cup of coffee. When the water has boiled he removes the element and rests it on a small polystyrene tray which held a cold chicken leg he had brought with him for a quick snack before going down to the local pub for the evening.*
>
> *He finishes his coffee and leaves the room, forgetting to turn the element off or unplug it. The element soon melts through the tray and comes to rest on the newspaper under it.*
>
> *The paper has started to smoulder when fortunately the floor housekeeper enters the room to deliver the extra pillow Mr Wisebanker ordered when he checked in at reception.*
>
> 1. What factors contributed to the fire?
> 2. What action would the housekeeper take?
> 3. What might the hotel management do to prevent such an incident occurring again?
> 4. What might have happened if the housekeeper had not entered the room?

4. Only collect handbags and other valuable or important personal possessions if these are nearby. Never attempt to collect belongings from elsewhere in the building. Guests must be dissuaded from going to their rooms to fetch valuables.

Special responsibilities
Some members of staff have special duties to perform if a fire breaks out. These may include:

- taking a list of all the rooms let with the names of the guests to the assembly point
- checking keys in and keys out, to give some idea of who is in the building
- taking all clock cards or the staff book to the assembly point as a record of which staff are on duty
- taking duty rotas for a roll call at the assembly point
- bringing the cash box out with them.

At the assembly point
Once at the assembly point remain there until told by a person in authority that it is safe to leave.

- Never return to the building to collect something.
- Do not return to the building to check for missing people. Inform the fire officer or someone in authority.

Guests, customers and other people who do not work on the premises, are particularly vulnerable when a fire breaks out.
- They are in surroundings they do not know.
- They may not have read the fire instructions in their room.
- They may not understand the language.
- In hospitals, the residents are generally infirm and will need extra help.
- In residential establishments they may be elderly, very young or disabled and will need special help.

Why you should remain calm
- Guests will take their cue from you. If you remain calm they are more likely to do the same.
- If people are allowed to panic the evacuation will be slowed down. People may trample on each other and cause injury or death.
- If people are orderly and quiet, fire officers are more likely to hear calls for help from those in need. Vital instructions from those in authority will be heard.
- You are more likely to make the right decisions and to perform your duties correctly if you are in a calm frame of mind.

!! REMEMBER
Smoke and gas resulting from a fire can cause unconsciousness in a few minutes. In smoky conditions:
- keep low, crawling along the floor if necessary, as smoke rises
- breathe as shallowly as possible through the nose
- in large rooms and corridors, keep close to the walls to guide you
- if visibility is poor, use the back of your hand to guide you, not the palm—you will be less likely to cut your hand.

Customers and staff have a right to feel confident that they and their possessions are secure and safe. Staff and management have a legal and moral duty to see that everything possible is done to reduce the risks arising from the actions or activities of:

- criminals and thieves
- other dishonest people
- terrorists
- violent or disturbed people, for instance muggers and rapists.

Providing security

When a new building is planned, careful thought should go into security aspects such as the design of doors, locks and windows. Unfortunately many buildings were designed and erected long before the security risks of the late twentieth century were even heard of. So many security features have to be added on afterwards which is always more costly and disruptive.

Thieves are often opportunist, that is, they do not plan a burglary, but seize the opportunity when it arises: a window left slightly open, a key carelessly dropped by a member of staff, or an inattentive person at the reception desk who does not notice who enters and leaves the building. There is a lot that employers can do to discourage theft, planned or otherwise, and it is up to staff to make sure they use the security systems provided correctly. For instance, a really determined thief may impersonate a customer in order to obtain the key to that customer's room. If front of house staff are unsure of the identity of the person, they should do proper checks before handing over any keys (see unit 27).

Hotel, catering, leisure and tourism establishments contain a lot of valuable stock from wines, spirits and cigarettes to food and linen, not to mention the day's cash takings and the possessions of guests and customers, all of which can tempt the burglar

Management and staff
- Access points to the building should be observed at all times, either by staff on duty at reception and staff entrances for example, or by closed circuit television. Entrances that are only intended for use at specific times must be securely locked at all other times.
- Fire exits can present a security problem, especially if they are the kind that can be opened easily from the inside and deliberately left open. All fire exits should be checked frequently to ensure they are properly closed (see unit 18).
- Storage areas should be effectively secured and adequate storage space should be available for valuables belonging to customers and staff.
- Don't talk to journalists or news reporters about the security precautions, or any security problems that have occurred. Never discuss such topics in pubs, restaurants, on public transport or in other places where you might be overheard.
- If you bring any valuables to work keep them safe in your locker while you are on duty. Keep lockers locked and the key in a safe place.
- Put all equipment and materials in the correct place after use. Storage areas must always be kept locked when unattended.
- All staff should be issued with a name badge, uniform or other suitable means of identification—carefully controlled to minimise the chance of someone pretending to be a staff member.
- Staff should not be allowed to take personal handbags, shopping bags or baskets into work areas. Such bags can be used to remove stolen items and to bring in personal stock such as bottles of spirit for sale in place of the management's stock, and all the proceeds pocketed.

‼	**REMEMBER**

Security arrangements must never hinder or make more difficult escape in the event of a fire.

- The identity of contractors, sales representatives, tradespeople, local authority officials, meter readers and so on should be checked before they are allowed access to the building. If the person cannot produce means of identification, phone his or her employer or supervisor to check.
- Deliveries should be supervised (and suitable delivery areas set aside) so that delivery personnel do not have unobserved access to any part of the building.
- Conference delegates and exhibition visitors should be issued with name badges so they can be readily recognised. This may mean insisting that the organisers make suitable arrangements.
- Mark valuable items such as video recorders and antique ornaments with invisible codes to identify their true owner.
- Ensure car parks and other areas where people might conceal themselves in the dark are well lit. It is also important to keep garden shrubbery trimmed and avoid planting bushes and trees so they allow an intruder to get into the building unobserved.

Security systems

Closed circuit television (often known as CCTV) to observe front and back public and staff entrances, delivery points, foyers and so forth. Modern cameras can be made to move, zoom in close on the subject, or carry out a continuous sweep of the area.

Invisible beams to span passageways, entrances, windows, etc. When the beam is broken an alarm sounds and/or a warning light comes on at the control panel.

Pressure pads fitted under carpets or floors at entrances, or in front of valuable objects, for example. An alarm or signal is set off when someone stands on or walks over the pressure pad.

Sensors which can be set to pick up for example, the vibrations caused by someone forcing a door or breaking a window, but which ignore normal disturbances. Another type of sensor can pick up the heat radiated by a person.

Luggage scanners, firearm and *bomb detectors* play an important role in maintaining security at hotels and conference centres used for party political conferences and meetings involving important government, diplomatic and business people and royalty.

Less sophisticated equipment also has its role. For example steel reinforced doors to storerooms, steel netting over the windows of ground floor storerooms, strengthened glass, strong door bolts and locks that cannot easily be picked or burst open, window locks, strong safe deposit boxes and securely located safes.

---

* FOR INTEREST

Most establishments have their own system of stock control, but dishonest staff have been known to abuse the system, stealing cash, drink, linen, food and other valuables. In fact some have set up elaborate systems to avoid being found out. Under-ringing is where dishonest staff ring up the total on a till out of sight of the customer, which allows them to 'under-ring' the amount and pocket the difference. Another trick is to bring in a bottle of spirits from outside, sell this in the bar in the normal way and pocket the profits. Deals between delivery drivers and staff receiving stock have also been known. The member of staff will sign that they have received, say, ten boxes of strawberries when in fact only nine go to the kitchen. The tenth never leaves the delivery lorry, and is sold by the driver who then splits the profits with the dishonest staff member.

 TO DO

At your place of work or an establishment of your choice, make a list of the areas where breaches of security are most likely to occur. What additional preventative action could be taken by the staff?

Front of house management and staff

- When guests are called to the telephone or reception by making an announcement on the public address system, the guest's room number should never be announced. 'Telephone call for Miss Zodiac of room 231' would inform everyone who hears the announcement what room the lady is staying in.
- Carefully control issue of keys and ask guests to produce their key card. If a key card system is not in use and the guest is not well known, ask the person to give his or her name as well as the room number (see unit 27).
- Ensure that guest registration forms are filled in properly. This will not only guarantee that the legal requirements are met (see *Guestcraft: Front of House Operations*) but help trace anyone who needs to be questioned for some reason.
- Provide facilities for guests to store their luggage, for example if they are vacating their rooms in the morning before the conference begins, but do not depart until the afternoon. Front office staff, particularly porters, should keep alert when a large number of people are milling around the foyer—new arrivals, group departures, people gathering for the start of an event and so forth. Do not allow unauthorised people into any rooms where guests' luggage is stored for safe-keeping.

Housekeeping staff

- Report discrepancies in room counts. For example:
  - rooms occupied when they should be empty
  - evidence that two people have slept in a room booked for one person
  - a room which should have been used but has not been
  - guests who seem to have left when they had booked to stay on for longer
  - guests who should have departed but have not.
- Staff servicing guest rooms should always work with the door open and keep their trolley by the door. If they have to leave the room for any reason the door should be locked.
- If a guest comes into a room which is being serviced, watch for signs that it is the genuine guest. If a man were to come into a room that is obviously only occupied by a woman, this should make the person cleaning the room suspicious.
- Report any missing towels, pictures, ornaments, television sets. Train yourself to check quickly that such items are all in place. If something is missing do not assume it has been taken away for repair or special cleaning—report it.
- Guest rooms should be inspected as soon as possible after the guests have departed, even if they cannot be cleaned immediately. In this way any missing items can be reported quickly—possibly before the guest has left the premises.
- Remove or arrange for used room service trays to be taken away for washing and storage as soon as possible. China and cutlery, for example, may disappear from trays left in corridors and guest rooms for long periods.
- Keep track of extras loaned to guests and ensure they are returned, for example irons, hairdryers.
- Keep linen chutes locked—they are not only a security risk but also a fire danger.
- Keep inter-connecting doors between guest rooms locked when the adjoining rooms are not let to the same party.

Restaurant and barstaff
- Ask customers not to leave bags, briefcases or other valuable items where they might be taken by an alert thief—for example on the floor or on a seat.

> > > **TO DO**

Speak to colleagues and friends of yours working in the hotel and catering industry and to anyone you know who regularly stays in hotels in this country and abroad. What experiences of property being stolen have they had or heard about? Can they tell you any stories about the ways in which hotel thieves have operated? Do they know of any hotel which has what they would regard as excellent security procedures, and if so, what was so good about them?

After getting as much information as you can by asking such questions, consider what additional points you could add to the security procedures given in this and the previous unit. Also note any security procedures you think should be added.

Observing people's behaviour

Watch out for and report anyone behaving in a suspicious manner, for example:

- hotel guests bringing empty suitcases into their rooms (possibly to pack items they have stolen from the hotel and/or other guests)
- members of a party of customers in the restaurant leaving one-by-one, possibly via the toilets, or making loud excuses that they have to rush off. There may be no-one left to pay for the meal!
- a 'customer' who seems unusually interested in what everyone else is doing or is hanging around without apparent reason
- sudden disturbances, for example a loud argument between two customers: the intention may be to distract the staff so they do not see an associate remove stolen property
- a person who cannot provide proof of identity, or who is very hesitant in providing answers when challenged in suspicious circumstances.

No private person has the right to search anybody. Unless agreement has been made by the staff, perhaps in their contract of employment, neither the employer, nor security or supervisory staff acting on the employer's behalf, can search staff or their bags. To lay hands upon another person without his or her consent could be regarded as an assault.

A private person can arrest someone when it is clear that an 'arrestable' offence has been or is in the process of being committed. Theft is an example of an arrestable offence.

Locking and leaving buildings

- Management and staff who work in premises that are closed for periods during the day, or at night, for example pubs, cafés and restaurants, should be particularly careful to check that the premises are empty before they lock up and depart. All rooms should be inspected including the toilets and each toilet cubicle. If there is any likelihood of being attacked, two people should make the tour together.
- All windows and doors should be checked (and their locks).
- Cash tills should be left empty and open—this will reduce the risk of damage if a thief does break in.
- Switch on security and burglar alarms before leaving.
- The police should be given the name, address and telephone number of the person who holds the key to the premises, and informed if the premises are going to be closed for a longer period than usual, perhaps because of holidays. If possible arrange for a security firm or reliable colleague to check the premises from time to time during long periods of closure.
- No keys should be left on the premises, unless they are locked in a safe or other secure place.

> ## ✳ FOR INTEREST
>
> Hotel foyers, restaurants and bars are favourite areas for criminals. Often working in twos or threes, one thief will distract the guest's attention while another snatches the luggage. Another trick is for the thief to join a queue of guests waiting to register or settle the bill. The thief then works the empty briefcase switch, exchanging an empty briefcase for the guest's identical (but hopefully full) one.
>
> The thieves choose times when the place is bustling with activity, such as the morning rush of guests paying their bills, or times when there are fewer staff than usual about and those that are on duty are likely to be busy preparing for the next busy period. So the lunch hours of 12 noon to 2 pm are popular with hotel thieves.

Taking payment

When handling *cash*:

- count the money carefully in front of the customer
- take special care when notes are given in payment to supply the right change. Some customers may confuse the staff so that it is difficult to remember if a £5 or a £10 note, for example, was handed over. Other people claim (falsely) that they gave over a higher value note. Cashiers in self-service restaurants, staff working in bars and fast food outlets should make a practice of stating the value of the note when it is handed over and leaving the customer's original note outside the till until the change has been counted
- look out for foreign coins: do not accept them as payment (unless there is some special reason) or give them as change
- check that notes are genuine. Many establishments instruct their staff to check all £10, £20 and £50 notes by holding them up to the light to see if the metal strip is present (to indicate the note is genuine). In some cases staff will ask their supervisor to check payment and change whenever a high denomination note is produced by the customer.

When accepting payment by *cheque*, check:

- the date: is the day, month and year correct
- does the amount in words and figures agree
- is the amount within the limit guaranteed by the cheque card (If it is higher, then the customer should be asked to pay the balance by cash or credit card, or the approval of your manager sought. In this situation never accept two cheques.)
- does the signature match that on the cheque card
- do the code numbers on the cheque and cheque card match
- was the cheque signed in front of you
- has the cheque card expired.

When accepting payment by *credit card*, check:

- is the card accepted by the establishment
- is the card on a list of lost or stolen cards
- has the card expired
- is the card in the same name as the client
- does the transaction require authorisation from the credit card company (most establishments set a limit on the amount that can be accepted without authorisation)
- have you filled in the voucher correctly
- does the customer's signature match the one on the card.

Taking cash to the bank

- Carry money in security bags.
- Use a vehicle if possible and transfer the money to the vehicle out of sight.
- Never establish a pattern of going to the bank at the regular time, or taking the same route.
- If possible take a colleague with you to act as a look out.
- Do not try to act heroically if you are attacked. Instead:
  - co-operate with the attacker, but giving away as little information as possible
  - note details about the attacker's physical appearance, manner of speech, any vehicle used, and the direction in which the attacker escapes (do not attempt to follow)
  - alert the police and your supervisor immediately
  - do not handle anything the attacker has touched to preserve finger prints.

Protecting guest valuables

Many hotels have a number of safe deposit boxes where guests can leave their valuables for safe-keeping. The deposit box can only be opened by using the guest's key and at the same time a master key held by the duty manager, or head receptionist. If there is a duplicate to the guest's key it is usually kept at a local bank.

Each time the guest uses the box a card is dated and signed and the guest's signature checked.

The valuables may be kept in a sealed envelope so that the contents remain unknown to the staff. If the hotel does not have deposit boxes, guest valuables may be kept in the safe.

‼ REMEMBER

Security is an important part of the service offered by a hotel, catering, leisure and tourism establishment. If the customer has been the victim of a theft or other unpleasant incident, the friendliness and efficiency of the staff, the excellence of the facilities will soon be forgotten, and it is unlikely the customer will ever return to the establishment again.

 **TO DO**

With a colleague visit three busy places in your local town, for example the railway or bus station during the evening rush hour, the square or high street on market day, and a popular lunchtime rendezvous for people working and shopping in the town. Watch how people take care of their shopping, handbags, briefcases etc.

When you have completed your exercise, design a poster which could go in a popular catering establishment to remind the customers to look after their belongings.

Alternatively, or in addition
If you work in or know an establishment which is closed up at the end of each day, discuss with someone in charge what the security procedures are at locking-up time. Then design a checklist which would remind anyone who has to take over the responsibility, for example on the proprietor's day off, of each important point.

Dealing with lost property

When customers' property, such as coats, bags and umbrellas, is left behind it should be handed in immediately to the supervisor. Staff who are aware of their customers will be able to give details of who was sitting where the property was found. When a customer returns to claim lost property, ask him or her for a brief description of the item. If you are in any doubt that the customer is genuine, or the lost property is particularly valuable, then ask your supervisor to take over.

Handling bomb threats

Report any suspicious packages or bags left behind. If you receive a bomb warning by telephone:

- Note the time of the call.
- Keep the caller talking for as long as possible while you try and get a colleague to alert the police.
- Get as much information as you can about the location, size and type of the bomb.
- Ask the caller to repeat the information.
- Listen carefully to the voice, noting the accent, whether calm/nervous, young/old, drunk/sober, male/female and so on; also note any background noises such as traffic, trains, machinery.
- Notify the police and your supervisor immediately.
- Note the time the call ends and write down all the details.

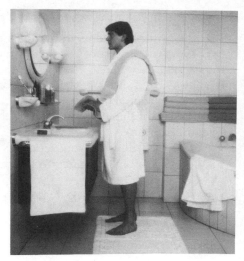

Most thefts from hotels and other buildings are carried out by guests and staff. Hotel property such as ashtrays, soap and towels are often removed under the guise of a little souvenir

Preventing violence

Often, when customers are violent or drunk, the reason can be traced to the way the establishment is run. Management and staff who are firm, though friendly, are less likely to have trouble because the customers will respect them and the rules of the establishment. Places where alcohol is served can be particularly violent. It is important to serve customers as quickly as possible, and to keep an eye out for any potential trouble.

Deal with any difficult situation calmly but firmly, if you feel able to. Otherwise alert the person in charge. Never get involved in any physical violence yourself.

Preventing drug abuse

Bars and other licensed premises are favourite places for dealing in drugs. It is illegal, and it is up to staff and management to be constantly alert to what is happening in the public areas. If drug pushers continue to get away with it, the establishment will become known in the neighbourhood as a place where drugs can be obtained, and it will not be long before the police are on the licensee's heels. The result to the establishment could be loss of trade and jobs, plus a large fine.

Dealing with a death on the premises

Housekeeping or room service staff may be the first to discover that the occupant of the room they have called to service has died, or appears to be dead (he or she may be in a deep coma).

A doctor should be called at once and the police informed (this will usually be done by the management as soon as the matter has been reported). The doctor and/or police will take care of arrangements such as informing the next of kin and removing the body. The housekeeping staff may be asked to help gather the dead person's belongings, making a record of them in case of any uncertainty later, and packing them ready for collection by the next of kin.

If a death does occur in the building, everyone involved will usually be asked to act as discreetly as possible to avoid upsetting customers and other staff.

▶ ▶ ▶ TO DO

Choose a hotel you know well and write a brief report describing how the responsibility for security is organised. If possible speak to some of the staff concerned. What do they regard as the main security threats? Does the design of the building, for example the number and location of exits, cause any special security problems?

✳ FOR INTEREST

Many large establishments employ *security officers* to:
- check any suspicious packages
- watch out for and check any suspicious people
- deal with anyone causing a security problem
- liaise with other members of staff over security matters and lost property
- supervise the control of keys
- supervise the movement of large sums of cash and valuables
- ensure that adequate fire training is given to staff and that regular fire exercises are held.

Ex-members of the police force are often employed as security officers, sometimes to work incognito so they can move among guests and staff more freely.

Timekeepers are sometimes employed at the back entrances to large buildings to:
- supervise the arrival and departure of staff
- inspect the property of individuals entering and leaving the building
- ensure that no unauthorised persons enter the building
- check deliveries.

It is often the role of *night porters* to act as security officers after the management have gone to bed or left the premises. They will usually be responsible for:
- locking outside doors (except fire exits, see unit 18)
- ensuring that all persons entering or leaving the building are authorised (late staff will enter and leave by the main entrance)
- checking that the building and its contents are safe throughout the night.

 SECURITY

Keys are one of the most obvious security risks. They can so easily get into the wrong hands. The loss of a key can mean the theft of all the items which were put under that lock and key. If a key is lost then the lock (or the barrel of the lock) will have to be changed.

Controlling the issue of keys to staff

To avoid the need for certain people to carry keys for a large number of doors, most establishments use a system of master keys.

- The *grand master* will open every lock even if it has been double locked. The general manager, duty manager or other senior member of management will usually be the only person to be entrusted with a grand master.
- The *master* will open every lock, but not one which has been double locked. The duty manager, executive housekeeper and chief security officer are the only people likely to be given a master key.
- The *sub-master* and *floor* or *section master* will open locks on a particular floor or wing of the building, for example, unless they have been double locked. (Sometimes these are known as *section* or *pass keys*.)

The master system means that the privacy of guests in a hotel, for example, can be protected. Anyone not wishing to be disturbed by housekeeping or floor service staff can double lock the door from the inside. The grand master can be used in an emergency.

A log book is kept with details of all key issues to management and staff. The date, time, name of person receiving the key and that person's signature are entered in the book. Similarly an entry is made on return of the key.

Management sometimes insists that keys are worn attached to the person responsible.

Controlling the issue of keys to hotel guests

Hotel bedroom keys must never be given out without first checking the identity of the person requesting the key. In some hotels, keys are only given out on production of a key card. A small card is filled in by the receptionist ready for the guest's arrival, or at the time the guest checks in. It will include such details as the room number, name(s) of the guest(s), date of arrival and departure and there is often space for the guest to sign the card. The card is then used by the guest to identify himself or herself when:

- signing bills to be put on the account
- collecting the room key
- settling the final account.

The receptionist, cashier or whoever is the last person to deal with a particular guest before he or she departs should remind the guest to hand back the room key.

Room keys which are left in doors or bedrooms should be handed to the front office. Anyone who finds a room key elsewhere should hand it to security staff or management with the details of where it was found.

Computerised key systems
Computerised key systems are used in more and more hotels to reduce theft and to minimise the expense and inconvenience caused when guests lose their keys or take them away with them. The key and lock are programmed at the time the guest is first issued with the key. The program is unique to the guest and to the guest's room,

> ## ✱ FOR INTEREST
>
> In some of the larger hotels, the senior management have a special lock-out key to prevent anyone else entering the room, for example if there are suspicious circumstances or the guest owes the hotel a large sum of money.

> ## ✱ FOR INTEREST
>
> In most hotels the bedrooms are numbered according to which floor they are on. For example all the rooms on the first floor are given numbers starting with a 1 (101, 102, 103 and so on). In some establishments the numbers are jumbled as an extra security measure, for example all the rooms on the first floor begin with 4 (401, 402, 403 . . .). This is sometimes more confusing for guests than for intruders!

> ## ▶ ▶ ▶ TO DO
>
> Ask your friends who work in hotels and also people you know who often stay in them as guests to describe to you the systems they have come across for controlling the use of keys to guest rooms. Do they think the particular system provides enough security for the guests? Have they come across any breakdowns in the system which would offer the opportunist or professional hotel thief a chance to gain access to guest rooms? Can they relate any stories to you about the tactics used by hotel thieves? Have they any suggestions for improving security?

so the key will not open any other door, nor will it work for the original room once the guest has checked out. If a guest loses the key the program is changed and a new key issued.

Some computer key systems use plastic cards, others plastic keys—both work in a similar way. Sophisticated systems are available which keep a record of what has been used to open each door, for example the guest's key card, the card issued to a particular member of staff and so forth.

Another system is linked to the bedroom heating/air-conditioning controls and the lights. This means that when the guest leaves the room the heating can be automatically turned down and any lights left burning are turned off, so reducing energy costs.

Staff have sub-master or section key cards which open certain doors

Other security measures

for staff
- Never leave keys in locks.
- Never leave keys lying around or in supposedly safe places such as desk drawers.
- Never lend keys to anyone else.
- Do not unlock a bedroom door for anyone who does not have his or her own key, unless you are quite certain that it is the person's room. Dishonest people can tell very convincing stories—so point out to the person concerned that you have to check their identity, because it is a rule of the establishment, made to protect the interests of guests.

for hotel management
- Never allow master keys off the premises.
- Establish a procedure for reporting faulty locks and catches and lost keys. If a key is mislaid, immediately have the barrel of the lock, or if necessary the whole lock, changed.
- Design key cards which cannot easily be forged and control stocks of blank key cards carefully so they do not fall into the wrong hands.
- Introduce a system so that if blank key cards do fall into the wrong hands, staff will recognise that they are not genuine.
- Do not number or label keys so it is immediately obvious to anyone who might find them what lock(s) the key will open.
- Do not mark key tags with the full name and address of the hotel, in case the key falls into the wrong hands. A PO Box number can be arranged with the post office so that keys can be posted back by guests should they take them in error.
- Store guest room keys so that no-one can easily tell which guests are out. Avoid displays of carefully arranged keys with large tags indicating their room number and boxes underneath that show the guest is out because a message is waiting.
- Provide a posting box at the front office so guests can leave their keys on departure without any danger of someone else picking them up off the reception counter.
- Install fittings so that bedroom doors shut automatically if they are left open and lock shut.
- From time to time arrange for all the lock barrels to be changed around. For example all the lock barrels on the third floor are exchanged with all the lock barrels on the first floor. This will confuse potential thieves who may have access to keys.
- Fit door chains to bedroom doors and/or spy holes (sometimes known as Judas eyes) so that guests can identify the caller before the door is fully opened.

✳ FOR INTEREST

In the film *Hotel* (based on Arthur Hailey's novel of the same title), a professional hotel thief adds to his collection of hotel keys by hanging around airport departure lounges and watching the travellers carefully so he can collect any hotel keys they drop in the litter bins rather than a mail box.

The same thief approaches the receptionist at a busy time and asks for the key to 4215. The receptionist hands him the key then a few moments later asks in a rather surprised tone 'But that's the key to the President Suite?' The 'guest' immediately apologises and explains he meant to ask for the key to 4251. In the meantime he has made an impression of the key, which he will put to good use later.

The owners, management and staff of hotel, catering, leisure and tourism establishments have a responsibility by law to maintain a healthy and safe environment for both customers and employees (see units 12 to 15). The law provides a firm framework of standards and protection, but accidents do still occur and employees cannot afford to become complacent when dealing with the welfare of people.

Ignorance of the law is no excuse. It is vital that staff know what their obligations are so that the health and safety of everyone who uses the premises is protected.

?? HOW TO

Prevent falls

- Keep floor areas clean and dry.
- Remove all hazards from the floor such as dirty linen and rubbish.
- Open and shut doors carefully.
- Walk, don't run.
- Wear sensible shoes on duty.
- Put up warning signs if cleaning floors or stairs or using a stepladder.
- Do not leave trailing flexes.

▶ ▶ ▶ TO DO

Speak to six people you know who work in the hotel and catering industry, if possible one from each of the following areas:

- kitchen
- restaurant
- bars
- housekeeping
- front of house/reception
- the stores or cellar.

Ask each person to name three accidents which are most likely to occur in his or her type of work. Analyse the responses to find out what are the two most quoted type of accident. Look through the appropriate units that follow (29 to 47) and draw up your own HOW TO PREVENT checklist for each of the two accidents.

Accident prevention checklist

Lighting should be adequate throughout the building, especially on stairways, corridors and where food preparation takes place.

Light fixtures, pictures and other ceiling and wall attachments should be securely fastened and in no danger of falling.

Stairs should be in good repair and have adequate, sturdy rails and bannisters.

Doors should not open into passageways where they could cause an accident. Fire doors should be kept closed (unless they are the type that close automatically).

Floors must be regularly and adequately maintained. Any frayed carpeting should be mended, uneven and defective floor boards and tiles replaced, and floors kept clean and free from grease and water. Any spillages should be dealt with immediately. Care should also be taken to remove any hazards such as rubbish from the floor. In busy areas it may be advisable to put down non-slip flooring.

Bathrooms and toilets must be regularly and carefully cleaned to prevent cross-contamination. Soiled towels and dirty soap should be removed. Sanitary bins and waste bins should be emptied frequently and any other refuse removed. Hand grips and slip mats in baths will reduce the likelihood of falls.

Shelves should be strong enough to bear the weight of the items stored. Heavy items should be kept on lower shelves and lighter items on upper shelves.

Stepladders should be provided for reaching high storage areas or those which require cleaning.

Breakages should be cleared immediately. If there is any possibility that broken pieces have entered food lying nearby, this food should be disposed of immediately.

Electrical equipment should be checked by engineers regularly to ensure it is safe and in working order. Plugs and sockets should never be overloaded. Ensure that hands are dry when using electrical equipment and switch off and unplug when the task is complete.

Rubbish should be removed regularly to an outside disposal area. Safety procedures for the disposal of potentially dangerous waste such as broken glass, razor blades and cigarette ends should be followed carefully.

Furniture, especially chairs and tables, must be in a good state of repair and regularly checked for splinters, sharp edges and broken legs.

Fire alarms, extinguishers and other fire prevention equipment should be regularly checked to make sure it is in good working order.

Exits, especially emergency exits, should be adequately marked and easy to locate. They should never be blocked, even for a short period.

Dangerous substances such as bleach, should never be stored or placed in cups or containers used for serving or storing food. All items should be clearly marked with their correct contents.

Utensils and other equipment should be used correctly and kept in good order.

✳ FOR INTEREST

Analysis of the catering accidents reported to one local authority over a year showed the causes to be:

	%
stairs	23
wet/greasy kitchen floors	20
slicing and mixing machines	19
burns and scalds	11
lifting heavy items	11
knives	8
use of ladders	5
moving furniture	3
	100

The accidents reported in a 300-bedroom hotel over a six week period included:

Chef: *burnt left foot* draining stockpot
General cleaner: *bruised back* tripped over electrical lead
Room cleaner: *broken wrist* slipped on bar of soap on floor
Night porter: *broken leg* slipped hurrying down stairs
Receptionist: *broken ankle* tripped on damaged stair carpet

Lifting heavy weights

Staff are often required to lift and carry heavy items. They may be cases, sacks, boxes, crates, furniture or piles of plates. Many back injuries, some of them permanent, are caused through lifting these items in the wrong way. In fact back trouble is one of the most common reasons for absence from work. There are some general rules to be followed if injury is to be avoided.

1. If the object is too heavy do not try to lift it without assistance from a colleague or by using a trolley or other lifting equipment.
2. Plan in advance how to lift the item and where it is to be placed.
3. Ensure that there is nothing in the way and that all doors are propped open. Give people plenty of warning about what you are doing.
4. Ensure that the eventual destination of the object is clear and that there is sufficient space.

Team lifting   Two or more people should work together to lift objects that are either to be placed on a high shelf, or are too heavy to be carried by one person.

One person should give directions on when to lift and where to move, to avoid confusion.

Lifting overhead   Lifting from the floor to waist level involves mainly the leg muscles which are fairly strong. Lifting objects above the waist and head also uses weaker arm and back muscles. In these cases it is safer for two people to work together, unless of course the object is very light.

Suitcases   When picking up suitcases, take special care as the weight may not be obvious.

1. Pick up the suitcase slowly and smoothly, not with a jerk which can cause a strain.
2. Bend at the knees until the hand, with an extended arm, reaches the handle of the case.
3. Do not risk injury by carrying too many cases at once.
4. Be careful not to knock into others while carrying cases in and out of lifts or around corners.

?? HOW TO

Lift a heavy object

1. Think about how to approach the job before attempting to lift.
2. Stand close to the object, with feet spread in a balanced position. If possible, face towards where the item is to be moved.
3. Keep a straight back and do not twist the spine. If it is necessary to bend down to lift the item, bend at the knees only, keeping a straight back.
4. Hold arms as close to the body as possible, keep the chin tucked in and place the fingers, not just the fingertips, firmly underneath the object to obtain a safe grip.

5. When a firm balanced hold is achieved, lift with a smooth action, straightening the knees and keeping the back upright.

6. When carrying the object keep it close to the body, with the back still straight.
7. Bend the knees again, not the back, to lower the item into position.

◆ ◆ ◆ TO DO

Practise lifting, pushing and carrying an object. Choose one that is not too heavy.

Using trolleys   When bulky or very large objects require moving it is usually safer to use a trolley or hand truck.

1. Do not overload the trolley and make sure that it is not stacked so high that there is no longer a clear view ahead.
2. When stacking the trolley, place larger, heavier items at the bottom so that the trolley is stable and smaller items are not crushed.
3. Pull trolleys or hand trucks through doorways rather than pushing them, ensuring that the coast is clear.

Using ladders

Ladders or stepladders should only be used by staff who have received training in their safe use, or are in the process of being trained and are directly supervised at the time.

Ladders should always be fixed securely so they will not slip or fall in any direction. They should not be so long or so flexible that they will sway and vibrate making it difficult to keep a safe balance.

- Single or extending ladders should be placed at an angle of 75° to the horizontal. The top of the ladder should be tied to the scaffolding or platform it is being used to reach, or secured by two guy ropes at 45° to the horizontal. It must be resting against a strong and stable structure. The foot of the ladder should be on a flat surface and staked to the ground. If the ladder cannot be staked to the ground, then it must be held in place while it is being used by a second person—however this is only safe if the ladder is being used at a height of up to 6.9 m (22 ft 8 inches).
- Stepladders must be fully opened out with all four feet resting securely on a flat, sound base.

‼️   REMEMBER

Always be careful when working at heights to:
- have only the equipment you need and can conveniently handle
- keep a safe hand-hold
- move the ladder as often as necessary so you never have to stretch or otherwise risk losing your balance
- tie or otherwise secure any equipment or materials you are using which might fall or get dropped accidentally and break something below or injure someone.

??   HOW TO

Push objects
1. Keep the back straight.
2. Keep the arms out-stretched in front against the object.
3. Keep the chin tucked in.
4. Tilt the body forward so that the rear leg, back and back of the head are in a straight line.

Heavy or bulk items should always be stored on low shelves or pallets, so that they are easily reached and it is not necessary to lift the objects above the head

Using electrical equipment

All electrical equipment is potentially dangerous and so great care should be taken when using it. The manufacturer's instructions should be followed precisely. The equipment should be maintained in good working order and regularly inspected by an electrician. If anything goes wrong, staff should report it to the person in charge so that accidents can be avoided.

- Do not use electrical equipment with wet hands.
- Check the flex, plug and socket before connecting equipment. Frayed flexes or broken plugs should be reported immediately, and equipment should not be used until the faults are mended.
- Do not use equipment that is known to be out of order.
- If electrical equipment begins to smoke or gives off a burning smell, switch it off immediately and report it.
- If an electric plug needs changing, inform the maintenance staff.
- Do not use electrical equipment unless proper training has been given.
- Ask for help when attempting to move heavy equipment.

Flexes and plugs
- Use the nearest socket and do not allow flexes to trail across busy work areas. Keep flexes close to the wall wherever possible.
- Do not use more flex than is necessary, or leave coils of flex on the floor.
- Do not let flexes trail in water.
- Ensure that electric sockets are switched off before connecting and disconnecting equipment.
- Do not remove a plug from a socket by pulling on the flex.

Be aware of the safety of others
- Keep equipment out of busy areas, and do not leave equipment where others may trip over it.
- Take care not to knock others when using movable equipment, such as suction (vacuum) cleaners.
- Do not leave equipment plugged in and unattended.
- Place warning signs where wet floors are being left.

After use
- Switch off machines using the switch on the equipment and disconnect from the wall socket after use, particularly at the end of a work shift.
- Put away movable equipment after use.
- Rewind flex correctly after use.
- Keep equipment free from dust, moisture and grease. Unplug machines before cleaning, removing dust bags or changing blades.
- Do not allow cleaning water to get into the machine's electrical equipment.

▶ ▶ ▶ **TO DO**

Take a look at two electrical machines used at hotel, catering, leisure and tourism establishments. Choose ones you are not yet familiar with, but might have to use in the future.

Read the instructions for their use. Speak to someone who trains staff in how to use them. Ask staff who use them regularly for their help. Make your own lists of points it will be useful to remember when you are given training in how to use the equipment.

Each item of machinery should have its own set of rules for safe use. Become familiar with them.

- Do not use equipment unless full training has been given.
- Staff aged under 18 should not clean dangerous machinery.
- Read the instructions on the machine before using it.
- If in doubt about how to operate a machine, seek help.
- Where safety guards are provided, these should always be used. Never operate machines with the guards off.
- Beware of sharp blades. These can be very dangerous, even when they are not moving.
- Hair should be covered and kept away from machinery. Clothing should be kept out of reach.
- Do not use equipment that is known to be faulty.

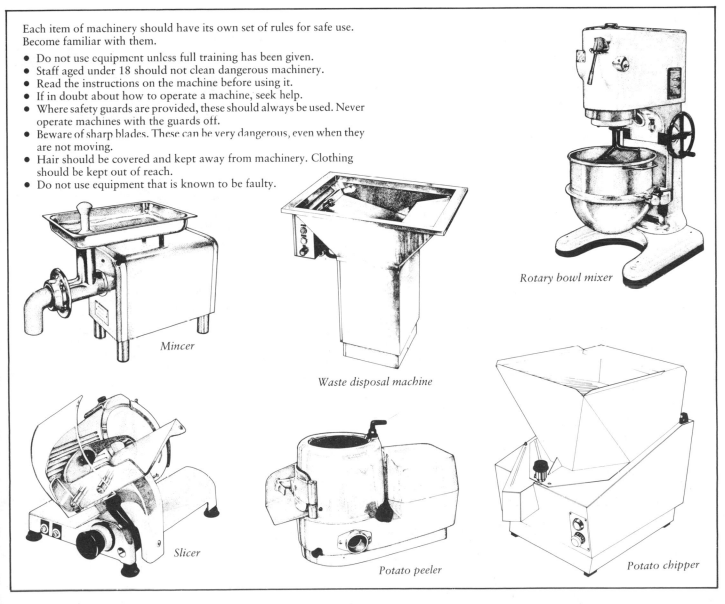

Mincer

Waste disposal machine

Rotary bowl mixer

Slicer

Potato peeler

Potato chipper

We clean to remove soil—dust, dirt, bacteria or any other unwanted matter on a surface, and to keep surfaces free of soil for as long as possible. Cleaning is also important for:

- *hygiene*—to control the spread of harmful bacteria which are the cause of disease and infection. Bacteria spread through dust, dirt and earth, air, water, refuse and human beings (through handling food with dirty hands, for instance).
- *safety*—to remove rubbish which may cause fire or injury if someone slips on it. Items which are well looked after will remain in a safe condition for longer than neglected ones. For instance dust in an air-conditioning vent is not only a fire hazard, but will also require the generator to work harder, eventually leading to a breakdown of the entire system.

> **Where does soil come from?**
> Soil can be brought into a building from outside in the form of mud, sand, smoke, fumes and pollutants. Other soil is formed within the building, for instance through sewage, or dirty cleaning practices. Management can reduce the amount of soil in a building by installing doormats at entrances, for example, and by insisting on high standards of hygiene from staff.

Cleaning properly

1. Use the correct cleaning agents, following the instructions for use carefully. Never top up cleaning solutions, but prepare fresh ones instead, disposing of the old solutions. Detergents and chemical disinfectant solutions (if these are used) should be disposed of down toilets or sluices.
2. Clean as frequently as required. The higher the standard of cleanliness to be achieved the more frequent the cleaning. Remember that over-zealous cleaning can damage surfaces.
3. Use cleaning equipment and procedures which will collect the soil effectively. For example use damp cloths not dry ones to dust surfaces—dry cloths, even the very soft absorbent ones, scatter dust. And use suction (vacuum) cleaners or special mop sweepers, not brooms to clean hard floors—brooms will also scatter much of the dust.
4. Do not risk spreading bacteria when cleaning. For example toilet brushes should not be carried from bathroom to bathroom in a hotel, but each bathroom should have its own toilet brush. Cloths used for cleaning toilets should not be used for any other purpose. Cloths used for dusting should never be used for wiping food surfaces. Soiled towels should never be used to polish glasses kept in guest bathrooms, or to dry crockery or glassware provided in the bedroom for guest use.
5. Take proper care of equipment: wash, dry and store correctly after use to prevent the spread of bacteria.
6. Keep high standards of personal hygiene: wash hands frequently, especially after cleaning toilets. Cover cuts and boils. Wear uniform or clean overalls at work. Never risk spreading an infection you are carrying to other people.
7. High surfaces should be damp-dusted before low ones.
8. Do any job which might spread dust first, such as changing sheets or moving furniture. Dust before suction cleaning.
9. When cleaning an area, start with the cleaner items and go on to the dirtier ones. This will avoid the spread of soil from dirty to cleaner surfaces.
10. Wash walls and doors from the bottom to the top. In this way any water running down the wall or door will run over a clean surface and not leave water marks.
11. Rinse surfaces well. Change rinsing water frequently.

Regular and correct cleaning not only makes a room or area look attractive, but it preserves and protects the decor, furniture, fittings and equipment

Cleaning routines

Many jobs in hotel, catering, leisure and tourism establishments involve some cleaning. Some, like housekeeping jobs, are almost entirely made up of cleaning tasks. Others such as reception work involve no more cleaning than making sure the reception desk looks attractive. But whatever job is done and whatever the type of establishment, some kind of cleaning routine is required. This will cover the cleaning tasks that must be performed after each use of a piece of equipment or utensil, to those cleaning tasks which must be done daily, weekly or periodically—monthly, three monthly and annually.

> *MASTERCRAFT*
>
> See *Housecraft: Accommodation Operations, Housecraft: Operations Workbook,* and *Housecraft* video *A Key to Operations.*

Examples of tasks

after each use
- washing knives, chopping boards and work surfaces after each food preparation task
- wiping spills, cleaning restaurant tables after the customers have left
- picking up rubbish, dropped items and other articles from the floor
- clearing food refuse and disposing of correctly

daily tasks
- cleaning bathrooms and toilets
- removing grease and dirt from kitchens and similar areas
- clearing ashtrays, waste baskets
- suction-cleaning floors
- washing kitchen floors

weekly tasks
- damp-dusting high shelves and door frames
- washing storeroom/cellar floors
- washing kitchen walls
- scrubbing and buffing hard floors
- defrosting refrigerators

periodic tasks
- washing windows and paintwork
- washing picture glass
- shampooing carpets
- stripping and polishing floors

How clean to clean

Standards of cleanliness vary with the type of establishment. For instance guests staying at an expensive hotel may expect higher standards than those staying in a caravan park, though neither place should present a health hazard under any circumstances. Hospitals require the highest standards of cleanliness, especially in operating theatres, intensive care units, premature baby units and infectious disease wards where the spread of dirt and bacteria would risk the lives of patients and staff.

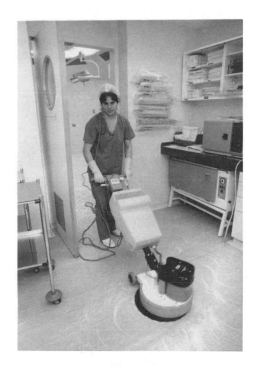

 TO DO

Who is responsible for the cleaning of a particular work area or for specific cleaning tasks within it varies considerably from one establishment to another. In a pub, for instance, part-time staff may be responsible for cleaning the customer areas and the toilets, and for washing the floor behind the bar counter and in the kitchen, while the barstaff are responsible for cleaning the shelves (including stocks of drinks on display), the drink dispense equipment and glass-washing, while the catering staff are responsible for cleaning the rest of the kitchen.

Write a short description of how the cleaning duties are organised in a hotel, restaurant, pub, hospital or leisure centre you know. If it is a large establishment and the organisation varies considerably from department to department, choose two contrasting departments.

Floors   Floors collect more dust and dirt than other surfaces, much of it brought in from people's shoes. Daily cleaning is essential. Special attention should be paid to hidden areas, such as wall and floor junctions, behind equipment and underneath tables and cupboards. Slippery floors can cause injury and so they should be kept free of wet or greasy substances.

Hard floors, such as linoleum, should be suction-cleaned, mop-swept or washed daily, depending on their usage. Carpets should be suction cleaned daily. Crumbs in the restaurant, for example, may be cleaned up between meal services using a carpet sweeper so as not to disturb any customers. Carpets should be shampooed at regular intervals, if necessary by an outside contractor.

When cleaning a corridor or staircase, clean one side at a time, so as to leave the other side free for people to pass. A warning sign should be placed in a prominent position to inform people that the floors may be dangerous.

Windows, doors, walls and ceilings   Windows and other glass surfaces should be cleaned at least every few weeks. Many establishments employ contractors to clean windows.

Routine cleaning with hot detergent water is sufficient to remove grease and soil on most doors, walls and ceilings. An outside cleaning company may be used to deal with any build-up of grease or dirt, or to 'deep-clean' kitchens on a regular basis.

Lighting   Light fittings need to be kept clean, especially the diffusers on fluorescent tubes. If the fittings are suspended, frequent cleaning of the upper surfaces is essential as these attract dirt and dust.

‼ REMEMBER

Never use chairs or stools to reach high areas. Use a ladder or stepladder (see unit 29).

Ventilation   Filters and ducts need regular cleaning because of the risk of fire from a build-up of dirt and grease.

Freezers, refrigerators and chill cabinets   These will need defrosting regularly, followed by thorough cleaning with detergent and hot water. Walk-in freezers or cold rooms should be washed out weekly to avoid accumulations of dirt and debris on the floor.

Food and drink preparation areas   Any area where food and drink is prepared requires the highest standards of hygiene: kitchens, restaurants, bars, still rooms, dispense bars and any other ancillary areas, room service pantries and cellars. All equipment and surfaces must be kept spotlessly clean.

Cleaning agents used on food surfaces or equipment must be rinsed away using plenty of clean water so that there is no residue left to contaminate other food later.

Toilets and bathrooms   Toilet bowls require cleaning using a toilet brush and appropriate detergent. The toilet seat, base and cistern should also be cleaned using a cloth reserved for the purpose. All hidden surfaces must be cleaned properly and inspected—a long-handled mirror is suggested in *Housecraft*.

In public toilets, hot air dryers or paper towels should be provided, or an automatic roller towel dispenser. If linen towels are provided, as in some luxury establishments, there should be enough towels available for each person to be able to use a clean one. The wastebasket should be emptied frequently.

Toilet chains, door handles and light switches which come into contact with hands should be cleaned daily.

Sanitary disposal bins should be emptied separately and the contents incinerated. This task is often carried out by an outside contractor.

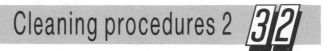

Kitchens must be kept spotlessly clean (units 37 to 42)

Waste gullies and traps Sink waste gullies should be checked and cleaned of any blockages. Traps used to collect tea leaves, grease and other debris need to be regularly emptied and cleaned.

Shelves and cupboards Food and utensils should be removed once a week or so in order that shelves and cupboards can be thoroughly cleaned. This includes damp-dusting the walls and both surfaces (top and underneath) of shelves. Cupboards used for long-term storage of dried or canned goods, or non-food items, should be cleared out and cleaned at least once a month.

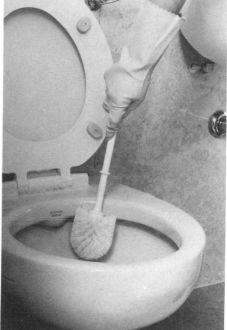

▶ ▶ ▶ TO DO

The cleaning procedures for any particular surface will take account of the material it is made of and the finish. Some wallpaper finishes cannot be washed, for example. And the procedure for cleaning chairs upholstered in a fabric is quite different from that used for leather chairs or for polished wooden furniture.

Choose four different surfaces, preferably ones you are not familiar with the cleaning procedures for, such as a marble table top, a glass partition, a wooden floor, a fabric-covered chair. Arrange with the housekeeper, domestic services manager or cleaning supervisor to watch them being cleaned. Make notes of the procedures and cleaning agents used and why they are considered to be appropriate.

Water helps to loosen and dissolve most dirt. But it cannot penetrate a dirty surface unless it is mixed with soap or detergent. Really heavy grease stains need a solvent-based cleaner rather than a water-based cleaner. Other dirt and surfaces respond well to abrasive cleaners.

Water   Water is the simplest cleaner of all. Applied under pressure it cleans hard surfaces such as outdoor walls and vehicles, and soft surfaces such as carpets. Water also rinses out dirt removed from a surface by another cleaning agent such as detergent.

Soap   Soap is made from fats mixed with caustic soda (alkali). When used with water it can break up most dirt, but it leaves a scum and so is unsuitable for cleaning most surfaces. It is used mainly for personal washing and for cleaning delicate materials such as wool.

Detergents   Synthetic detergents are made from chemicals mainly derived from petroleum. When mixed with water they:

- enable water to penetrate, for example, a greasy surface
- can break up a body of dirt into fine particles which it then coats preventing the dirt from reforming and sticking to the surface again.

The surface is finally rinsed in clean water to remove all traces of dirt and detergent.

There are three kinds of detergents:

Neutral detergents (sometimes referred to as general-purpose detergents) are made from strong alkalis and weak acids. They are often green or straw-coloured and are used for washing dishes, damp-dusting and mopping and for similar routine cleaning tasks. They are generally safe for all purposes.

Alkali detergents (also called hard surface cleaners) are used for heavier or more specialised tasks such as removing ('stripping') polishes from vinyl floors. They are corrosive and can damage surfaces and should be used with care.

Acid detergents are sometimes used for cleaning toilets, for removing lime stains for instance in the toilet bowl at water level. Strong acids such as hydrochloric acid used to clean toilets can damage the skin and most surfaces. They should never be mixed with other cleaning agents because this can produce a chemical reaction which releases harmful gases into the air. Weak acids such as lemon juice and vinegar are useful for removing rust and persistent stains on baths.

Solvents   Solvent-based cleaners dissolve heavy grease and oil which water-based cleaners cannot cope with. The contain a solvent such as methylated spirit and detergents, and are used as paint strippers, furniture polish, stain removers and for dry cleaning.

Abrasives   Abrasive cleaners (or scouring cleaners) are used mostly for cleaning enamel and ceramic basins, baths and tiles. Available in cream, liquid, paste or powder form they contain finely ground sand, pumice or chalk which rub away dirt. Abrasive powder is much coarser than liquids, creams or pastes, but all of them can damage surfaces. They should never be used on plastic or acrylic baths, for instance, because they will leave scratch marks.

> ▶ ▶ ▶ **TO DO**
>
> Make a list of the cleaning agents which are at your workplace or college, indicating alongside each product the task it is used for.

Chemical disinfectants Chemical disinfectants may seem the obvious agent to use for killing bacteria (and advertising in the media generally supports this view). In most cases, however, they are not usually necessary. If a surface has been cleaned properly, most bacteria will be removed, along with most of the dirt and other matter which encourage the growth of bacteria. (Remember: the surface should be left dry, as moisture also encourages the multiplication of bacteria.)

Occasionally chemical disinfectants are used, for example in hospital wards where infectious patients have received treatment, but then only after cleaning (disinfectants cannot clean surfaces and disinfect at the same time).

Chemical disinfectants designed to kill bacteria will only work if stored and used correctly.

- No single disinfectant is effective on all bacteria, so be sure to find out the correct disinfectant for the specific range of bacteria to be eliminated.
- Disinfectants take time to do their job.
- Disinfectant solutions will lose effectiveness if they are kept, in some cases for more than a few hours.
- Some chemical disinfectants will be inactivated by certain plastics, cork and other materials.

✳ FOR INTEREST

Although chemical disinfectants are often used on floors, normal thorough cleaning will remove most bacteria and those that remain are usually harmless. In any case it has been shown that within hours or sometimes minutes after disinfecting a floor, it reverts to its pre-disinfected state.

If toilets and drains are cleaned efficiently there is no need to use a chemical disinfectant.

Smells, so often a reason for using chemical disinfectants, are more effectively dealt with by improving ventilation and cleaning.

?? HOW TO

Use cleaning agents

1. Always wear protective gloves when working with cleaning agents because they irritate and burn the skin.
2. Always wash hands after doing any cleaning.
3. Dilute the product according to the manufacturer's/workplace instructions. Use right amount for the task.
4. Use the weakest agent first. Only if the dirt proves stubborn, use a stronger agent.
5. Never mix products because this may produce harmful gases.
6. Do not pierce an aerosol can, even if it appears to be empty. It may explode.

The manufacturer's instructions will explain

- dilution rates: too concentrated will damage surfaces and is wasteful, too dilute will not do the job properly
- how much time to give the cleaning agent to work
- how to rinse dirt and cleaning agent from the surface
- at what temperature the agent works best
- how to store cleaning agents when not using them
- any safety warning such as to wear protective clothing
- how often to use the cleaning agent
- how to dispose of used cleaning agents.

Storing cleaning agents

- Keep away from foodstuffs.
- Close all containers firmly after use.
- Store containers upright.
- Always store in a correctly labelled container.
- Where products are bought in bulk, they should be decanted into clearly labelled containers with instructions on each for use.
- Store in a well ventilated cupboard or room, away from fire risks.

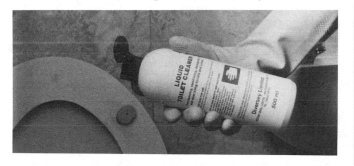

Vermin and insects spread disease. They are particularly dangerous in kitchens, restaurants and storage rooms where they may contaminate food and drink which is then eaten by human beings, and in linen stores, bedrooms and other accommodation areas where they can spread harmful bacteria and even attack people.

Most establishments rely on the expertise of a pest control company or the local authority to eradicate pests and to carry out regular inspections to ensure the premises are rodent free. However staff can do a lot to prevent infestations by maintaining high standards of hygiene and cleanliness and immediately reporting any signs of pests:

- droppings
- footprints in dust or on food
- gnaw marks and damage such as holes in sacks
- holes and nesting sites
- dark, greasy marks on walls or pipes that suggest rats frequently use that route
- the pest itself—dead or alive.

Why pests must be controlled

- To prevent the spread of disease. Pests carry harmful bacteria, especially in faeces and urine which are dropped on food as they eat.
- To prevent the waste of food. A sack of flour, for example, which has been attacked by rodents will have to be disposed of immediately.
- To prevent damage to property—gnaw marks on cupboards or holes in furniture, for instance, gutters and downpipes blocked with bird droppings.
- To comply with the food hygiene regulations. The Prevention of Damage by Pests Act (1949) requires all establishments to notify their local authority of any pest infestation.

What pests need

In order to survive, pests require food, shelter, warmth and security. If they are denied any of these they will die, or move to another area.

Food   Pests eat food found in kitchens, restaurants and other catering establishments. This may be in the form of crumbs, left-over food ready for disposal and food which is being stored, prepared and even served.

Shelter   Pests need protection from extremes of weather. Buildings provide an ideal place with their networks of pipes, nooks and crannies.

Warmth   Pests are attracted to buildings which are warm. Central heating pipes and warm kitchens make ideal breeding grounds.

Security   Pests need to be safe from predators, including human beings. Occupied buildings contain plenty of small hidden areas where pests are secure.

How to control pests

By stopping them from entering the premises or area
- Keeping areas well-lit and ventilated.
- Repairing damage to fixtures and fittings promptly.
- Closely investigating any evidence of drain failure or blockages and repairing any defects as soon as possible.

- Storing items on open shelves rather than cupboards (which are dark and offer protection to pests).
- Filling in gaps in skirting, around drains and closing gaps under doors.
- Boxing and ducting pipes.
- Laying a plastic jelly on ledges and sills to discourage birds from perching near windows and other points of entry to the building, or keeping them away using netting.

By depriving them of food
- Keeping the premises clean and tidy.
- Clearing spillages promptly.
- Keeping pest-proof lids on containers.
- Disposing of waste frequently, especially food waste, and storing waste away from the building.
- Keeping food covered whenever possible during preparation, display and service.
- Ensuring all areas are accessible for cleaning and inspection.
- Treating food containers with care to avoid damage.
- Storing goods away from walls, windows and ventilators which attract pests, and above floor level, for instance on pallets, low stands or shelves.
- Keeping storage areas pest-proof and in good repair.
- Cleaning and inspecting before new stock arrives.
- Rotating stock, so the older stock is used first.
- Disposing of infested goods.

By poisoning them
- Placing pellets or powders which contain poisons in infested or vulnerable areas. Some poisons are combined with cereals, fruit, fish, meat or other bait to attract pests.
- Using insect and fly sprays.
- Using electronic insect killers. The ultra-violet light attracts the insects and the electronically charged grills kill them.
- Applying a special long-lasting, non-staining insecticide to walls and ceilings.

By trapping them
- Baiting and setting traps to attract and catch mice and rats.
- Hanging sticky paper which insects are attracted to and get stuck on to.

!! REMEMBER

Insecticides and other pesticides are poisonous. They can cause serious illness if they are consumed by human beings. They should never be used where there is a risk of contaminating food.

Some pest control substances can be used in food areas, but food and food equipment should be cleared well away from the area before treatment and surfaces should be thoroughly cleaned afterwards.

If in doubt, call in a professional pest control company and leave the job to the experts who know the pests, the problems and the precautions.

▶ ▶ ▶ TO DO

Arrange to join a tour of inspection for pests at your workplace or college. Ask your supervisor/the pest control expert to:

- tell you what pests he/she is particularly looking out for
- identify any pests you come across and explain why they are harmful
- point out any signs of pest infestation
- explain how the pests are controlled in your building.

There are four groups of pests which can present a problem in hotel, catering, leisure and tourism establishments:

- rodents—rats and mice
- insects—flies, wasps, cockroaches, mosquitoes, silverfish, spiders, ants, moths, carpet beetles, beetles which eat food, woodworm, bedbugs, fleas, head lice
- birds—mainly pigeons, sparrows and starlings.

Rats and mice Rats are creatures of habit. They follow regular paths to and from food, usually keeping close to walls and pipes. The typical brown rat weighs about 400 g (1 lb).

Mice are more erratic. One mouse can feed from as many as 200 different points in a night. A mouse can climb a vertical surface and squeeze through a gap no wider than a pen barrel.

Rats and mice need to keep their teeth sharp. They do this by gnawing at hard materials. They will damage gas and water pipes and electric cables, often with disastrous results.

Flies The common housefly is the most widespread of the winged pests. Flies breed rapidly. One female can lay 25 to 150 eggs at a time and produce six such batches in her (short) life.

Flies have an eating tube instead of a mouth. When they want to eat they vomit a drop of stomach fluid through this tube on to the food. After a few moments they suck the fluid back up, along with the nutrients it has dissolved – leaving behind large numbers of microorganisms. In this way flies will spread harmful bacteria that cause food poisoning and diseases such as typhoid and dysentery.

Wasps At their most active in Britain in August and September, wasps often seek out sweet food and syrups. They are a nuisance, may carry bacteria and if provoked will sting people.

Cockroaches Most premises can be entered by these (usually) brown or black insects which can squeeze their way through the narrowest cracks. They generally keep out of sight until it is dark when they emerge, often in many hundreds, from their hiding places. They leave an unpleasant smell and carry many harmful microorganisms in their gut and on their feet and bodies.

Mosquitoes Sometimes a nuisance in hot summers, mosquitoes breed in stagnant water such as ponds, neglected garden containers and water butts. They feed off human blood, and their bites leave a very irritating small lump on the skin—some people will swell up badly.

Silverfish These silver-grey insects are about 12 mm (½ inch) long and cigar shaped. They occasionally move about during daylight, but prefer darkness. Silverfish are not known to carry any harmful bacteria, but they can damage cotton or rayon fabrics and in large numbers are a nuisance. They mainly feed on starchy substances such as flour products, paste in wallpaper and book bindings, and starched clothes. They like damp conditions so their presence may indicate a damp problem.

> > > **TO DO**
>
> Ask among catering staff you know what pests they have seen at their workplaces. Did they recognise them (you may be able to help)? Do they know what harm they may cause (again you may be able to help)? What control measures were taken to deal with the pests?

The common cockroach

Beetles There are a variety of troublesome beetles. The bread or biscuit beetle sometimes occurs in residues or crumbs trapped in crevices. Flour bags sometimes contain the flour beetle. Hide beetles, spider beetles and larder beetles are scavengers attracted to meat and protein products.

The flour mite is very troublesome. Heavy infestations in flour cause a musty smell and greyish colour and the flour has to be discarded. The spider beetle is also very small and will infest dry ingredients. It thrives on pieces of spilt dough and neglected spills of flour.

Woodworm The common furniture beetle lays its eggs in cracks and crevices of unpolished wood and in holes caused by previous woodworm activity. On hatching, the larvae or 'worm' eats its way through the wood, taking from two to three years to reach the surface and maturity as a beetle. It then bites its way into the open air, leaving a tiny hole.

Bedbugs Capable of surviving many months without food, bedbugs can hide in bedding, furniture and even books. They deposit their eggs in cracks, crevices, behind wallpaper and in other inaccessible places. Although bedbugs do not fly, they can cover considerable distances, emerging in the darkness of the night to feed off any human blood they can find. Their bites leave large red patches and cause swelling.

Fleas If pets are allowed on the premises, fleas can infest bedrooms, cloakrooms and even the public areas. Although they are only 2 mm long ($\frac{1}{16}$th inch) they can jump great distances. Adult fleas feed on blood. Their bites are irritating, affecting some people quite seriously.

Head lice As their name suggests, head lice live mainly in the hair of the head. They suck blood. Their numerous eggs or nits stick so firmly on to the hairs they cannot be brushed or combed out.

Birds Birds carry bacteria, especially in their droppings. Their nests attract insects which in turn become a health hazard.

Spiders Frightening to some people, spiders also spin their webs in corners and around fittings where they may escape the notice of cleaning staff but can offend those customers who do notice them.

Ants The tiny reddish Pharaoh's ants are often found in centrally heated buildings, introduced perhaps in a delivery of dried fruit. They are so small they may not be noticed until they are well established and start swarming over food in large numbers. Pharaoh's ants can carry harmful bacteria (see box).

Garden ants also have an acute sense of smell and will quickly find and infest exposed food of every kind.

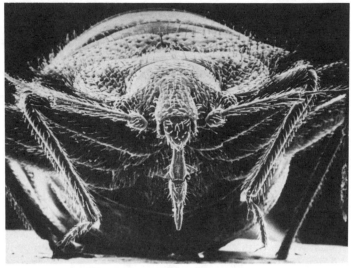

Bedbug swollen after meal of blood

Moths Clothes and house moths in their winged state are harmless and rarely live for longer than a month. However one female may lay up to 200 eggs, choosing a dark, warm undisturbed place such as blankets and clothes put away in storage, or corners of carpets or upholstered furniture. The eggs hatch and become grubs (caterpillars) which immediately start feeding on the material. They stop feeding when they are fully grown—the entire life cycle of a moth varies from one month to two years.

There are also several types of mill and flour moth. These can find their way into stores and their grubs will feed on such foods as nuts, flour, cocoa, chocolate, cereals and dried fruit.

Carpet beetles Adult carpet beetles are often seen in Britain in April to June when they find places to lay their eggs. The beetles are between 2 and 4 mm long ($\frac{1}{16}$ and $\frac{3}{16}$ inches) at this stage and their favourite breeding places are storage cupboards, carpets and carpet underlays. The grubs which hatch from the eggs (often called 'woolly bears' because of their appearance) are most active in October, feeding on wool, hair, fur, feathers and anything made from these products. Carpet beetles are now considered to be more troublesome than moths.

✱ FOR INTEREST

- One fly may be carrying as many as two million bacteria when it lands and vomits on food.
- One mouse will shed about 70 droppings every day and as it has no effective bladder will dribble urine most of the time.
- Pharaoh ants caught on hospital premises were found to be carrying 19 species of harmful bacteria.
- Four or five people die each year from Weil's disease contracted from water, straw or other material polluted by rats.

Waste looks unattractive. It may smell unpleasant. It is a risk.

- Cigarette ends and waste paper are a fire hazard.
- Sharp objects such as broken glass and razor blades are a safety hazard.
- Waste foods attract pests and encourage harmful bacteria.
- Business documents and confidential papers are a security risk.
- Used sanitary towels, syringes and clinical waste are a hygiene risk.

Waste should be disposed of in such a way as to minimise health, hygiene and safety risks.

Dealing with waste

When it is a fire risk
Paper, rags, cigarette ends and aerosol cans should be kept separate from other dry waste and kept in non-flammable containers. Ashtrays should be emptied into special metal bins with a lid. These should not be used to collect other rubbish. Aerosols should never be incinerated, as they will explode at high temperatures.

When it may cut someone
Bottles, broken glass and crockery, and used razor blades should be carefully wrapped before placing in the bin, or should be disposed of in a separate waste unit. Hospitals use special 'sharps' boxes for scalpels and syringes.

When it will attract pests
Food waste, grease and sticky substances should be placed in waste receptacles with tight fitting, pest-proof lids, or ground up in a disposal unit.

When it is a hygiene risk
Sanitary towels should be burnt in an incinerator, or specially treated using a germicidal fluid. Hospitals use different colour bags and bins to distinguish between hazardous and general waste.

When it is confidential
Documents and business papers which might be of interest to other people should be burnt in an incinerator or shredded and disposed of with the dry waste. The burning or shredding should be supervised.

When it is dry
If dry waste has to be stored indoors for a time it should be kept in metal bins to reduce the risk of fire (see unit 18). Dry waste can be collected in plastic or paper bags providing it is taken out the building immediately to the refuse collection point. If possible it should be compacted (made to fill as little space as possible) to make collection easier. Where large quantities of paper and cardboard are used, a compaction unit may be used to compress the waste into manageable bales.

When it is wet
The best type of container for wet waste waiting collection outside is a metal or plastic bin with a close-fitting lid which keeps out pests.

Wet waste which has to be stored indoors for a time can be placed in plastic bags (mounted on stands with lids), plastic or metal bins. The bin stands for plastic bags must be cleaned daily, and plastic or metal bins washed out each time they are emptied (which should be at least daily).

Plastic bags should be replaced when they are between two-thirds and three-quarters full, tied up and taken to the outside refuse collection point.

Some establishments have disposal units fitted beneath the outlet of sinks, or free-standing heavy duty models. These grind most waste matters into small particles and despatch them down the drain. Waste disposal units should have a safety device so they cut out if cutlery or similar items are hidden in the waste. They should also be easy to dismantle, clean and maintain, otherwise deposits will build up inside harbouring bacteria and causing unpleasant smells.

> ### ▶ ▶ ▶ TO DO
> Carry out an investigation into what happens to the waste at your place of work or an establishment of your choice. What types of waste are there? What receptacles are used for collection? How often is the waste collected?

!! REMEMBER

- Wash your hands after disposing of rubbish or handling the lid of a waste receptacle.
- If you have to search through rubbish for some reason, wear heavy gloves with a long cuff.
- Different types of waste should be collected and stored separately until they can be disposed of. Receptacles used for the storage and collection of food should not be used for other refuse.
- Rubbish should be collected up frequently and not left to accumulate.
- Some items may be recycled such as soap, rags, bottles and paper. Care must be taken to deliver the items to the proper collection points.

The outside refuse area

The collection area should have non-porous, well-drained concrete to make washing down easier. Stand-pipes, hoses or some method of swilling down the refuse area with water should be available.

Refuse areas should be away from the premises so that flies do not enter food rooms. But they must be close enough for staff to take out waste without undue effort.

Dustbins should be stored under cover and off the ground, for example on tubular steel racks, to make cleaning easier and to discourage pests.

They should have tightly fitting lids to prevent pests gaining access (see units 35 and 36).

Depending on the volume of waste generated by the establishment, waste may be collected as often as once a day. The refuse area must be large enough to give access to large refuse collection lorries.

Heavy duty wheeled bins

Kitchen staff owe it to their customers, their colleagues, and their company to ensure their health and safety while they are on the premises. High standards of hygiene are particularly important where food is prepared, in order to avoid food poisoning. Nearly all cases of food poisoning can be avoided if proper care is taken over:

- personal hygiene (see unit 8)
- preventing cross-contamination (the transfer of food poisoning bacteria from raw food to cooked food)
- temperature at which food is stored (see unit 38).

Great care must also be taken in kitchens to avoid cuts, burns and scalds, and falls on slippery floors. Much kitchen equipment is dangerous.

The legal requirements on food hygiene are comprehensive and strict (see units 16 and 17).

See *Foodcraft* books and videos.

Checklist for food preparation staff

Personal hygiene

Keep yourself clean and tidy.

Keep fingernails clean, trimmed and free of varnish.

Store outdoor clothing and footwear in a proper storage area, well away from food handling areas.

Wash your hands regularly: when coming on duty, after leaving the kitchen or handling raw food or going to the toilet, and after meal and rest breaks when you have been eating, drinking or smoking.

Do not wash food or food equipment in wash hand basins, and do not use food sinks for hand washing.

Before you sneeze or cough, hold a disposable paper tissue over your nose and mouth and wash your hands afterwards.

Cover cuts or abrasions with a blue waterproof plaster.

Use a clean spoon for tasting food and wash it after use. Never taste food with your fingers.

Do not lick your fingers or touch your nose, mouth or hair.

Never smoke or spit in food handling areas.

Do not sit on work tables

Report any illness or infection (see units 15 and 17).

Cross-contamination

Never allow utensils (including chopping boards, knives, and slicing machines) which have been in contact with raw food to be used for cooked food unless they have been thoroughly washed.

Wherever possible knives and chopping boards should be reserved for specific uses and colour-coded. For example: blue for raw fish, white for dairy products, turnip-coloured for vegetables and red for meat.

Keep raw foods well separated from cooked foods, for example, raw meat and poultry should be stored in a different refrigerator from cooked food.

Emergencies

Fire risks are high in kitchens were gas burners, fat fryers and other cooking equipment is used. One in every five fires in catering establishments is caused by insufficient cleaning of filters and ventilation ducts above cooking equipment.

Staff should be trained in fire fighting so that they know what to do in an emergency. It is important to know the correct fire extinguisher to use according to the type of fire (see units 18 to 22).

Most catering establishments rely on an effective stock control system to keep a check on food, equipment and other items which are necessary in the kitchens. When everything that is issued to and from the kitchens is accounted for, then this information can be linked to the establishment's purchasing and sales control

The temperature of food

Keep food at temperatures which are too low for rapid growth of bacteria, that is below 10°C (50°F), or too high, that is above 63°C (145°F)—see units 38 and 47. If the food has to be in the critical temperature zone, this should be for as short a time as possible. So food should be served immediately after it has been cooked. If it has to be chilled because it is to be served cold, for example, the cooling process should happen as fast as possible (within 90 minutes) and the food refrigerated to prevent bacteria from reproducing. If food is reheated this should be done quickly and thoroughly, to a high temperature. (See unit 38.)

Test that food is at a safe temperature by using a temperature probe. Always sterilise the probe after use.

Safety

Wear sensible non-slip shoes which cover and protect the toes (with steel caps). Wear safety clothes issued to you, such as a chef's double-fronted jacket and apron. Follow manufacturer's and workplace instructions when using equipment.

Do not use equipment unless you have been trained, or are in the process of being trained in its use (see unit 14).

Report any faults and make sure that faulty equipment is not used by clearly displaying an 'out of order' notice.

Do not allow flexes to trail across floors or food preparation surfaces.

Never overload sockets with too many plugs.

Never use electrical equipment with wet hands. Do not use electrical equipment near sinks (see unit 30).

Take special care when using mixers, mincers, slicing machines, microwave ovens, deep fat fryers, pressure cookers and other dangerous equipment (see unit 42).

Never use a knife like this (see unit 41)

 FOR INTEREST

The London Marriott hotel, winner of one of the *Caterer & Hotelkeeper/Ecolab* Clean Kitchen Awards, put down its success to the staff. "Staff are the hotel's number one asset and we have to show them that we care about them and what they do."

The priorities of the Marriott's cleaning programme are:

- to guarantee the health and safety of everyone who eats in the hotel
- to provide a clean, safe and pleasant working environment for the hotel's staff
- to strive continually for higher standards by training the staff to use the correct amount and type of cleaning agent for each job.

But keeping the hotel's quarter-of-a-century-old kitchen clean is a non-stop process. Notices all round the kitchen remind staff to 'Clean as you go'. Spot checks are carried out regularly during the day and there are more thorough checks at the beginning and end of each day. Once a week every area of the kitchen and every piece of equipment is thoroughly checked. Photographs are sometimes taken on these inspections—of misdemeanours as well as of achievements—and displayed at monthly staff meetings. They have proved a useful means of ensuring standards do not drop.

 **TO DO**

Design your own poster to remind food preparation staff to 'Clean as you go'.

Alternatively

Ask if you can photograph with the help of someone in charge, some examples of good and bad cleaning practices in a catering kitchen. Then use these to make teaching aids which would help train new staff and remind existing staff.

3|8 HEALTH, HYGIENE AND SAFETY

More on food poisoning

One of the reasons for cooking food, apart from making it more digestible and palatable, is to kill harmful microorganisms which may be present in the food.

The greatest danger is food-poisoning bacteria. There can be literally millions of these present on the food, but they are completely invisible. The food looks, smells and tastes perfectly normal. The way to make sure that these bacteria are kept harmless is strict temperature control. Food-poisoning bacteria are killed at temperatures above 63°C (145°C) and grow slowly at temperatures below 10°C (50°F).

If for some reason, food is to be first cooked and then stored and reheated, control of microorganisms, especially bacteria, is even more important than in normal cooking procedures, because the food goes through the critical temperature zone three times.

Reducing the dangers when food is chilled and later reheated

Most catering establishments follow the recommendations laid down by the Department of Health in *Chilled and Frozen: guidelines on cook-chill and cook-freeze catering systems* (1989), available from HMSO bookshops (ISBN 011 321161 9).

at point of entry
The food purchased must be of prime quality. It must then be stored under strict conditions of hygiene.

initial cooking
The centre or core of the food must reach a temperature of at least 70°C (158°F). Some experts recommend 75°C (167°F) as an even safer internal temperature.

portioning
Portioning should be carried out quickly and hygienically whether the food is hot or cold. The size and shape of the container should be selected for fast chilling. The depth of the food in the container should be no more than 5 cm (2 inches). The containers must be clearly labelled with date of cooking, number of portions and reheating instructions.

chilling
Food must be chilled within 30 minutes of cooking and reduced to a temperature of 0 to 3°C (32 to 37°F) within a further period of 90 minutes.

portioning after chilling
In some establishments the food is chilled in multi-portion containers then plated before reheating. The portioning process must then be carried out within 30 minutes of the food leaving chilled storage and before reheating starts, at temperatures under 10°C (50°F). It is then reheated to at least 70°C (158°F) on the plate on which it is served.

storage
The chilled food must be stored in a special refrigeration area and never next to other fresh or conventionally prepared products. The temperature must be monitored regularly and immediately adjusted if it varies.

reheating
The food must be heated as quickly as possible to a minimum internal temperature of 70°C (158°F), but ideally to 75°C (167°F). Food which is not eaten shortly after reheating should be destroyed. It should never be re-chilled, frozen or reheated again.

Food which is not reheated and eaten within five days (including the day of preparation) must be destroyed.

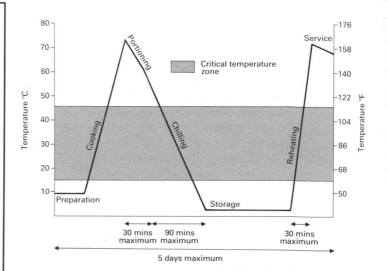

Using frozen meat

Frozen meat, especially poultry, should be thoroughly defrosted and then cooked through to the centre. If it is to be served hot it should be eaten as soon as possible after it is cooked. Most harmful bacteria are destroyed at temperatures above 70 to 75°C (158 to 167°F) and so meat should reach this temperature right through to the centre. It should never be cooked one day and reheated the next, because this means it will pass through the critical temperature zone at least four times—defrosting, cooking, cooling, reheating. Cooking in one step discourages the growth of bacteria because the meat will pass through the temperature danger zone only twice—defrosting followed by cooking. For this reason meat pies and pudding containing raw meat that has been frozen should always be eaten immediately after they are cooked.

High risk foods

Foods which are high in protein, such as fish and meat, or which are to be eaten raw, such as shellfish, are particularly prone to contamination by bacteria because they provide an ideal feeding and breeding environment. Some foods are contaminated before they arrive in the kitchens, in which case thorough cooking, and correct storage and preparation are essential to avoid serious cases of food poisoning.

Meat and poultry Although contamination can start through unhygienic practices, some food is contaminated before it reaches the kitchen. Poultry is the cause of most reported cases of food poisoning, mainly through bacteria called salmonella, which attacks the chicken while it is still on the farm. Salmonella can be destroyed with thorough cooking, making sure the heat reaches right to the centre of the bird or other meat.

Shellfish Shellfish may become contaminated from the sewage polluted waters in which they grow. Bacteria can also be introduced to shellfish through poor handling, and because they are eaten raw they are a common cause of food poisoning.

Eggs The shell is likely to be contaminated by bacteria, which could be dangerous if allowed to penetrate into the egg. Some eggs are already contaminated by salmonella before they leave the farm. All eggs should be refrigerated, and cooked thoroughly before being eaten. Foods containing eggs which are eaten raw, such as mayonnaise, are particularly risky.

Milk Milk is an ideal medium for the growth of bacteria, and so special care should be taken to store and handle it hygienically. In Britain all cows must be tuberculin tested. As an extra precaution most of the milk sold to caterers and the public is pasteurised (heated very briefly to high temperatures, then rapidly chilled again).

Vegetables Vegetables should be washed thoroughly in cold running water to get rid of earth which contains many varieties of bacteria (see unit 39) and other foreign matter.

‼ REMEMBER

- Food can also be contaminated by foreign bodies such as nails, packaging materials, hairs, cigarette ends and glass, and by chemical and other poisonous substances used in cleaning.
- Some varieties of mushrooms and berries are poisonous. Rhubarb leaves should not be eaten for the same reason.
- Some pulses, for example kidney beans, are poisonous if not cooked properly. Follow instructions.
- Food handlers who are ill or carriers of salmonella or the hepatitis A virus are likely to contaminate food.
- The human body is a source of the food poisoning bacterium, *staphylococcus aureus*, in particular the nose, hair, cuts, boils and sores.

▶▶▶ TO DO

Prepare and cook a meal of your choice, and make a list afterwards of all the precautions you took to avoid contaminating the food. These would include, for instance, washing of your hands frequently, cleaning the chopping board and knife after cutting raw meat, washing raw vegetables thoroughly. Where do you think you could improve your standards of hygiene, personal and in the way you work?

During the 1970s and 1980s the trend in the number of reported cases of food poisoning has been upwards: 22,200 in the first half of 1989 compared with 15,700 in the same period in 1988. Most of these incidents happen to single individuals, but general outbreaks do occur, for instance, when all the guests at a function have eaten the same food.

Despite the fact that it is a legal requirement to notify cases or suspected cases of food poisoning, the cause of some incidents is never identified. It is suspected that many more cases are not reported.

Cases of food poisoning: average number over four years

Establishment	Incidents per year
restaurants, hotels, banqueting halls	86
hospitals	34
prisons, welfare institutions	20
office/factory cafeterias/ dining rooms	10
schools	8

In a survey carried out in 100 catering kitchens of all types of size, involving analysing 5000 samples, it was found that although many surfaces looked clean they were badly contaminated. The survey (carried out by a UK-based hygiene and pest control firm) found contamination of 100 million bacteria per square centimetre in the worst areas. (Depending on the degree of risk in the area of activity, 10, 50 or 100 bacteria per square centimetre is a realistic safe standard.)

- In preparation areas:
  - 65% of the chopping boards
  - 54% of the refrigerator door handles
  - 40% of the work surfaces
  - 75% of the sink draining boards
  examined were contaminated.
- In the cooking areas, one-third of the work surfaces were contaminated and 30% of hot cupboard door handles.

A study of food poisoning cases showed the causes to be, in descending order:

- preparation too far in advance
- storing or holding food at room temperatures for too long
- inadequate cooling/refrigeration
- inadequate reheating
- insufficient cooking
- holding food in hot cupboards too long
- cross-contamination
- inadequate thawing.

▶ ▶ ▶ TO DO

Choose one example of a catering practice you know of and which is likely to cause food poisoning. For example:

- Roasting joints of meat or poultry a day in advance, allowing them to cool overnight in the kitchen, then carving or jointing and finally warming through with a little gravy on the serving dish.
- Bringing meat and fish required for the day's menu out of the cold room/refrigerators first thing in the morning and several hours before it is actually prepared or cooked.

Work out, with the help of your tutor or supervisor if necessary, another way of producing a safer and better end-product for the customer.

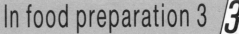
Food poisoning bacteria and symptoms

Salmonella (over 40 different types)
Occurs in the intestines of many animals and humans, pets, flies, cockroaches and other pests. Raw meat, poultry, fish, eggs, meat products such as sausages and unpasteurised milk are often contaminated when they arrive in the kitchen.
Symptoms appear 6 to 72 hours (usually 8 to 48 hours) after eating, and include abdominal pains, nausea, vomiting and diarrhoea. These can last for seven days or more and very old, very young or sick people can die of salmonella poisoning.

Staphylococcus (various strains)
Occurs in infected cuts, sores, boils and inflamed throat conditions, on normal healthy skin, especially on the face and hands and in the nasal passages. Poor personal hygiene—unwashed hands, leaving cuts or boils uncovered and coughing or sneezing over food—can transfer it to food. Staphylococcus is destroyed by normal cooking, but if it has been allowed to multiply on food it produces a heat-resistant toxin that cannot be destroyed even by thorough reheating. This is why great care must be taken with partly-prepared dishes. Cold meats made into sandwiches, salads, or sliced for cold platters, milk, egg products and and artificial cream are easily contaminated with staphylococcus.
Symptoms appear 1 to 6 hours after eating and may last for up to 24 hours. They are relatively mild, but include nausea, abdominal pain, diarrhoea and vomiting.

Clostridium perfringens (or clostridium welchii)
Occurs in the intestines of animals and many humans. It also occurs in raw poultry, meat, in water and in the soil (therefore on vegetables). When conditions are unfavourable for the growth of this bacterium, it forms heat-resistant spores which can resist normal methods of cooking, even, in some cases, boiling for five hours. In certain conditions, for example slow cooling of food (this includes normal refrigeration as opposed to rapid chilling in a special fast chiller), storage of food at room temperature, inadequate or quite slow reheating of previously cooked food, the spores can reactivate and start growing again. Food poisoning is caused when large numbers of bacteria are eaten. The bacteria multiply and produce spores and a poisonous chemical or toxin.
Symptoms appear 6 to 22 hours after eating and last for 12 to 24 hours. They include abdominal pain, headaches, diarrhoea and (rarely) vomiting.

Clostridium botulinum
Occurs in inadequately processed vacuum packed (sous-vide) foods, canned or bottled foods. The bacterium grows in foods in the absence of oxygen and produces a poisonous toxin. It occurs in the soil, in meat, meat products, fish and shellfish.
Symptoms appear 12 to 36 hours or longer after eating. Botulism is usually fatal. Unfortunately the first symptoms are similar to those caused by other food-poisoning bacteria: nausea, vomiting, possibly diarrhoea, fatigue, headaches and dizziness. By the time the second stage has been reached (constipation, difficulty in swallowing, breathing and speaking, and double vision) it is probably too late to save the patient. Death may result in 1 to 8 days.

Bacillus cereus
Occurs in rice, cereals and vegetables. Long moist storage at warm temperatures will allow the spores to reactivate and the bacteria can then multiply.
Symptoms appear either 1 to 6 hours after eating and include nausea, vomiting and some diarrhoea, or 6 to 16 hours after eating and include acute diarrhoea and occasional vomiting.

Campylobacter
Occurs in under-cooked poultry, sometimes as a result of it not being defrosted thoroughly and unpasteurised milk.
Symptoms appear 1 to 11 days after eating, and include abdominal cramps, followed by foul-smelling, bloody faeces.

Listeria monocytogenes
Occurs in soil, from which it is transferred to vegetables, poultry, meat and raw milk (i.e. unpasteurised). It also thrives in damp places such as dishcloths. It can grow at temperatures below 5°C (41°F).
Symptoms are not typical of food poisoning. They range from a mild flu-like illness in most people to meningitis. For pregnant women, and people whose immune systems are not functioning properly, it can be serious. If a pregnant woman becomes infected, her baby may die.

Bacteria clinging to the point of a (greatly magnified) chef's knife

40 HEALTH, HYGIENE AND SAFETY

Regular checking is accepted by many caterers as the key to good kitchen hygiene. A typical routine might include:

daily checks of
floor
walls
work surfaces
hot cupboards and bains-marie
food mixers
deep fat fryers
slicing machines
utensils
chopping boards

weekly checks of
ceiling
cupboards
drawers
drainage channels
ventilation ducts
ovens and steamers
refrigerators and cold rooms
storage bins

monthly checks of
lighting
high-level surfaces (e.g. tops of fridges)
shelves
deep freezers
machinery (in-depth check)
building and drainage generally

!! REMEMBER

Disinfection is not a substitute for thorough cleaning (see unit 33). The uncontrolled use of chemical disinfectants, so-called detergent-sterilisers and so forth, may encourage the growth of resistant microorganisms.

?? HOW TO

Cool food which has just been cooked

1. Use a fast chiller if one is available.
2. Then place the food in a refrigerator at 1 to 4°C (34 to 39°F).
3. If a fast chiller is not available, put the food as quickly as possible in a refrigerator or cold room after it has cooled down sufficiently—to about 10°C (50°F). Ensure this is done within 90 minutes of completion of cooking.

  - Place the food in a cool room and cover it to keep out airborne bacteria, flies and other pests.
  - Keep the food away from other foods, especially raw foods.
  - It is possible with some foods, for example stocks, custards, soups and other liquids partly to immerse the saucepan or bowl in a sink of cold running water. The sink outlet is fitted with a special pipe to stop the water level rising above the rim of the food container.
  - Keep joints below 2½ kg (5½ lbs) in weight so cooling does not take too long.
  - Never place uncovered food in front of open doors or windows.
  - Never leave the food to cool in the warm kitchen.

4. Do not keep food which has been cooked and chilled in this way for more than three days.

Defrost frozen food

1. Use a special thawing cabinet if one is available. This will provide uniform and carefully controlled conditions and keep the food covered.
2. If a thawing cabinet is not available:

  - Place the (covered) food in a cool room or leave it overnight in a refrigerator. (Thawing in a refrigerator always takes quite a long time.)
  - Never immerse frozen food in water to speed up defrosting. The outer surface of the food may thaw quickly, but the centre will remain frozen. If the food is left in the water long enough for the centre to defrost, the outer surface will have been held at a dangerously warm temperature encouraging the growth of bacteria.
  - Do not allow the liquid from defrosting foods to drip on to work surfaces or other foods.

3. After thawing, cook immediately or store in a refrigerator.
4. Cook defrosted food within 24 hours.

Choosing kitchen equipment

Surfaces of equipment in contact with food should:

- be non-toxic, that is not harmful or poisonous
- not react to the food or any substances in the food
- not react to materials or agents which might be used in normal cleaning
- be non-porous so they will not absorb foods
- be resistant to corrosion so they will not rust or disintegrate
- not chip, flake or crack and so absorb food (which will become a breeding ground for bacteria)
- be easy to clean.

Stainless steel is one of the most suitable metals for pots, pans, working surfaces and other similar equipment. Plastics, especially those that can withstand high temperatures, have many desirable properties.

Copper is not suitable, except for boiling sugar, but tin-lined copper saucepans are favoured by many chefs. The tin lining must be regularly renewed.

Aluminium equipment is inexpensive but some acid foods such as rhubarb can cause it to corrode. If used to make white or pale coloured sauces, aluminium may cause them to become grey. Aluminium substances in large quantities are believed to affect certain functions of the human brain. Plastic spoons (heat-resistant if necessary) should be used to stir foods being cooked in an aluminium container.

Glass and china, because of their fragile nature, are used in some kitchens for mixing and storing food only.

Wooden boards should not be used. Many chefs are now replacing wooden mixing spoons and rolling pins with plastic products.

Kitchen design checklist

Floors should be non-slip, durable, impervious and easy to clean. Good quality quarry tiles laid in acid-resisting cement are a good choice. Wooden floors are not suitable, nor are most types of lino. Sawdust or sheets of cardboard should never be used on kitchen floors. If something has been spilled on the floor it should mopped up immediately

Walls should be smooth and impervious and easy to clean. Coving between walls and floors should eliminate corners where dirt can accumulate. Well-grouted glazed ceramic tiles are suitable for kitchen walls, so is stainless steel sheeting (provided there are no gaps or spaces where dirt can collect).

Equipment should be easy to clean (stainless steel is one of the most suitable materials). Wherever possible, equipment should be easy to move, so that the floor underneath and wall behind can be properly cleaned. Fixed equipment should be fitted so that there are no gaps or spaces to collect dust. Alternatively it should be possible to clean underneath and behind it—a distance of 10 to 15 cm (4 to 6 inches) is recommended.

Equipment should also be of the right working height. It is dangerous when staff have to stretch to reach equipment.

 **TO DO**

Arrange with your supervisor or tutor to have look around a newly-built/recently converted/refurbished catering kitchen. Make a note of all the features which are designed to make cleaning and general maintenance easier.

Alternatively

Visit the show room of a catering equipment distributor or manufacturer. Explain your interest and ask if you can have a look at the equipment on display. Note the features which are designed to make cleaning and general maintenance easier.

Much of the equipment used in kitchens is potentially dangerous. Knives have sharp blades, cookers have hot burners, fryers contain bubbling fat. Dangerous bacteria can grow anywhere—on dirty surfaces, cloths, pots and pans, refrigerators, and sinks. It is therefore essential that all kitchen staff know what the dangers are and how they can avoid them. All equipment and utensils should be used properly, and kept scrupulously clean and in a good state of repair.

Knives

One of the most important skills that kitchen staff, especially chefs, have to learn is how to use a knife correctly. It is essential to know which knife to use for which job—dicing, shredding, carving, boning and so on. Using the wrong knife can lead to accidents. They must be kept clean and sharp because a blunt or greasy knife is more likely to slip. A dirty blade can also lead to cross-contamination, which is a health hazard. When not in use knives should always be kept in a safe place where they will not cause injury.

The most hygienic knives have waterproof handles which can be sterilised. The handle is made of two pieces riveted together through the metal that forms the knife blade. In less expensive knives the blade is attached to the end of the handle and may snap off with heavy use. The blades are made either of carbon steel or stainless steel. The advantage of stainless steel is that it does not rust or stain, unlike carbon steel which will stain if used on certain foods such as hard boiled eggs or onions. However, stainless steel is harder to keep sharp.

▶ ▶ ▶ TO DO

Make a list of as many types of knife you can find in the kitchens of your workplace or a catering establishment of your choice. You may need to ask staff what they are called and which tasks they are used for. If possible observe how they are used.

?? HOW TO

Sharpen a knife

1. To sharpen a knife using a steel, hold the steel steady in one hand, pointing away from the body and upwards at a slight angle.
2. Holding the knife with the point end of the blade away from you, sweep it along the steel, starting from the base of the steel and the end of the blade nearest the knife handle and moving the blade diagonally across the steel until you reach the tip.
3. Repeat, using alternate sides of the steel, until the blade feels sharp.

Some people like to move the knife towards the body. Others prefer to use a knife-sharpening machine or special block made of carborundum stone.

To test that the blade is sharp, run your thumb crosswise over the blade. If it is sharp you will feel a distinctive rasping sensation. Take great care not to run your thumb in the same direction as the blade because you could cut yourself.

Anyone who uses a knife should take care

Knife safety checklist

Do not walk around carrying a knife. If this is unavoidable hold it close to the body with the point facing downwards, and the blunt edge facing in the same direction as you are walking. Some chefs have special cases for keeping knives in, and this is the safest way, not only of storing them, but also of carrying knives around the kitchen. Put knives down so the blade lies flat and does not project over the edge of the surface.

Do not leave a knife hidden in a pile of partly prepared food, or in a bowl or sink of water to be washed later. Wash it immediately, or leave it in a safe place where it can be clearly seen.

Do not try to catch a knife if you drop it. Let it fall to the floor and then pick it up by the handle.

When wiping a knife after use, make sure the blade is facing away from the hand. Wipe from the blunt to the sharp edge away from the body.

Clean knives during and after use, to prevent cross-contamination and to avoid transferring the taste of one food to another. The handles should always be clean and free from grease to avoid them slipping out of the hand.

Never use a knife with a loose handle.

Always keep the knife sharp because this is safer and less likely to slip than a blunt one.

Always use the right knife for the right job.

Always use a cutting board.

When using a knife always pay full attention to the job you are doing.

Very dangerous machinery

Some machinery used regularly in kitchens needs extra special handling, for example, mincing machines, rotary knife chopping machines, dough mixers, vegetable cutters and potato chippers. Staff must, by law, be trained to use such equipment, and people under the age of 18 are prevented from doing the hazardous job of cleaning it. (See unit 14.) Again, it is essential to follow the manufacturer's instructions on use and maintenance. A notice to this effect should be displayed nearby. Safety guards should always be used where they are provided. Hair and clothing should be kept well away from machinery.

?? HOW TO

Use a tin opener
1. Clean the top of the tin.
2. Remove the paper wrapping, either entirely or from around the top so that it will not get caught in the opener.
3. Cut around the lid completely.
4. Remove the lid with a blunt utensil (if you use a knife it may damage the blade).
5. Empty the tin.
6. Rinse the inside of the tin and the lid with water.
7. Put the lid in the bottom of the tin and place the tin in the appropriate waste bin.

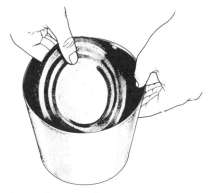

Remember to wash tin openers regularly, so that any food which is caught on the opening mechanism does not taint other food or become a breeding ground for bacteria.
Tip If storage for waste is limited, remove the bottom of the tin after the tin has been emptied and rinsed. Then squash the tin almost flat. Place the lid and bottom into the partly squashed tin so they will not cut through the waste bag or injure anyone handling the rubbish.

Equipment such as cookers, mixers, and fat fryers should be kept scrupulously clean, and never left unattended when in use.

Equipment safety checklist

Cookers and ovens
Always use dry oven cloths when carrying items in and out of the oven.
Stand clear of the door when opening a hot oven, and close it again as soon as possible.
Take care not to stand directly in the path of the steam when removing lids from hot pans.
Never leave pan handles over a flame or protruding over the edge where they may be knocked.
Ask for help to remove heavy pans from the stove if necessary.
Make sure that electric and gas rings are turned off after use. Do not burn electric and gas rings in order to warm the kitchen on a cold day.
When igniting a gas pilot light, stand to one side and check first that there has been no build up of gas. Afterwards make sure that the pilot light has been properly lit.

Deep fat fryers
Clean regularly to prevent a build up of grease which is a fire and health hazard.
Check the thermostat, which controls the temperature of the fat, regularly. Overheated fat can burst into flames.
Never overfill the fryer, either with food or oil. If fat boils over it can cause horrendous burns because it is far hotter than, say, boiling water. It will actually cook the skin just as it does a piece of chicken.
Food should be as dry as possible and lowered slowly into the fryer to avoid the fat overflowing and spitting.

Pressure cookers
Watch the pressure gauge during cooking.
Allow steam to escape before opening.

Microwave ovens
Pierce food which has a skin, such as tomatoes, potatoes, apples and whole trout, before placing in the microwave, otherwise it will explode splattering all over the inside of the oven. So never try to boil an egg in a microwave!
Take care when thawing food in a microwave oven that the centre is thoroughly thawed out before cooking.
Never switch on a microwave oven when empty because this will damage the machine.
Check the door alignment and locking mechanism regularly.
Metal or tin foil containers can cause a sparking effect in microwave ovens which, if it happens repeatedly, will damage the machine.
Do not put polythene bags, plastic wrapping film (unless it is labelled as suitable for use in a microwave oven) or containers made of metal or ordinary glass into the microwave oven.

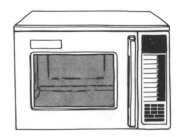

Washing up

The most hygienic way of washing up is by machine, but many establishments provide facilities only for washing up by hand. Provided this is done correctly it is a perfectly acceptable and hygienic method.

Washing up by hand
- Wear rubber gloves for hygienic reasons and to protect the hands.
- Wash all items as soon as possible to prevent food sticking to the surface.
- Scrape left-over food from plates and empty the dregs from glasses and cups before placing in washing-up water.
- Sort items into glassware, plates, cups and cutlery so that they can be washed separately.
- Wash glasses one at a time to prevent breakages and injury to hands. It is difficult to see glass in water and glassware could easily collide together and break when being washed.
- Items should be washed in water at a temperature of at least 60°C (140°F), and rinsed in clean water at 75 to 85°C (167 to 185°F) to kill any bacteria (this is too hot for the hands and so a basket may have to be used to lower items and lift them out again).
- Use the correct amount of a suitable washing detergent, following the manufacturer's instructions.
- Use clean nylon brushes, not cloths because these harbour bacteria.
- Do not dry items with a cloth. They should be allowed to dry naturally. Once dry, glasses and knives can be polished with a clean service cloth if necessary.
- Chipped, cracked, stained or broken items, which harbour bacteria and can cause injury, should be put to one side, and once they have been accounted for, they should be disposed of.

Washing up by machine
Industrial dishwashers work automatically, washing, rinsing and drying items. However they are unable to remove encrusted dirt and grease, and so some pre-washing by hand may be necessary. To prevent breakages and injury, and to make sure items are washed hygienically, they should be stacked correctly in the baskets. Only the recommended detergent and rinsing solution should be used.

Serving staff have to work closely with their colleagues in the restaurant, the kitchen and sometimes the bar. The pressures build up to a peak at service time, when the staff are likely to be dealing with many different customers at a time—customers who are perhaps unfamiliar with the establishment and would therefore need special guidance in the case of an accident. So it is particularly important that serving staff:

- carefully follow all working procedures required by the establishment, by law and by the manufacturers of equipment used
- keep the work areas safe by, for instance, removing all used plates to the washing up area as soon as possible rather than letting dirty crockery pile up on the sideboard, or on tables
- report promptly any equipment requiring repair or maintenance, for example, a rip in the carpet or a loose tile on the floor
- notify supervisors immediately of any accident, however minor.

Emergencies

If, despite all precautions, an accident does occur, then staff should know what to do. The correct action at the right time can save a life, say if a customer chokes on their food. In many establishments one member of staff will be properly trained in first aid, and will deal with any emergency treatment before professional help arrives, but all staff should be able to deal with an emergency when it arises, and know how to treat the more common injuries such as minor cuts, bruises, burns and scalds (see units 50 to 60). A first aid kit should be kept in the restaurant, and any accident should be reported to management and recorded in the accident book (see units 13 and 50).

Serving staff should also know where fire extinguishing equipment is located and how to use it. In large establishments regular fire exercises are held to ensure that staff know how to help customers evacuate the building in an emergency. In all establishments staff will be given regular fire instruction and they should know what responsibilities they, management and colleagues have in the event of a fire (see units 19 to 22).

MASTERCRAFT

See *Servicecraft: Food and Beverage Service, Servicecraft: Table Service Workbook* and *Servicecraft: Counter Service Workbook*.

?? HOW TO

Prevent burns and scalds

- Treat hotplates, gas and spirit lamps carefully, and turn off when not in use to avoid burns.
- Keep handles turned away from busy areas.
- Use dry cloths to hold hot plates.
- Take care when using matches.
- Take care with lighted candles on tables and buffet displays.

Prevent falls

- Keep floor areas clean and dry so people will not slip.
- Load trays carefully so that items will not fall off.
- Remove all hazards from the floor, such as dirty linen and electric cables.
- Open and shut doors carefully to avoid knocking anyone in the vicinity.
- Carry things in such a way that you can see where you are going.
- Get help to carry heavy items.
- Always walk—never run.
- Use the correct doors for going in and out between kitchen and restaurant.
- Wear sensible shoes on duty.

Prevent cuts

- Take care when using knives.
- Keep sharp articles away from serving areas.
- Clear up broken glass or china immediately, wrap it in newspaper or other strong material and place in a bin or special receptacle for the purpose.

▶ ▶ ▶ TO DO

Visit a restaurant or café of your choice and note how food is displayed and served. Is it kept covered before and during service? How is it kept hot or cold? Are you satisfied with the standards of hygiene? If not, list ways in which they could be improved. Then discuss these with colleagues.

Hygiene checklist for serving staff

Cover food before and during service to avoid contamination by dust and insects, and from people coughing and sneezing.

Keep cold food in the fridge until it is required.

Avoid using hotplates to heat food. They should be used only to keep hot food hot.

Serve food promptly to customers once it is ready.

Clean up any spills as soon as they occur.

Use a clean service cloth to polish glasses and cutlery, never a napkin or tablecloth.

Use separate serving utensils for different food items, and a clean set each time a dish is served.

Wash cutlery, crockery and glasses in hot water with detergent at 60°C (160°F), and then sterilise them in clean, very hot water at 80°C (180°F).

Always hold cutlery by the handle, plates by the rim, cups by the handle, and glasses by the stem or base, thus avoiding the surfaces which come into contact with the mouth.

Never re-use food which has been served to customers, such as uneaten bread rolls.

If you are unsure about the freshness of left-overs, do not store them to be served to customers or staff later. Dispose of them immediately.

Always serve hot food on hot plates, and cold food on cold plates to discourage the growth of bacteria.

Cutlery that is dropped on the floor should always be returned for washing.

Store cutlery in racks or drawers with the handles facing the same way.

Never use cups and other containers, normally used for food and drink, to store disinfectants and solvents. These and other poisonous substances should be stored in marked containers well away from food areas.

Never serve food which has been dropped on the floor.

Collect waste regularly and place in easily cleanable bins or other containers in a safe position.

Keep service areas and table tops spotlessly clean.

Never serve food that has been displayed the previous day because the conditions under which it has been kept may have encouraged the growth of bacteria.

Make sure you keep high standards of personal hygiene in the restaurant and kitchen, by not smoking, eating, sneezing, coughing, or scratching.

It is essential to have high standards of hygiene in the restaurant because without it, the food and drink which is served can become contaminated. If anyone consumes this food or drink he or she will become ill with food poisoning, and may even die

Flambé lamps

A number of accidents have occurred in restaurants where flambé lamps are used fuelled by liquefied petroleum gas (LPG). The disposable gas cartridge has ruptured, allowing flammable gas to escape on to hot surfaces and ignite. Serving staff and members of the public have been burned, some seriously.

Following one such accident the restaurateur was successfully prosecuted by a local authority for breaches of the Health and Safety at Work Act. The owner had failed to:

* make adequate arrangements for the handling and storage of the gas
* provide sufficient instruction, training and supervision in its use
* prepare an adequate health and safety policy and to ensure it was carried out
* ensure that customers or non-employees would not be exposed to risk.

The Health and Safety Executive has advised caterers to take certain precautions.

1. Change disposable LPG cartridges only when the lamp is cold and in a safe place away from any possible source of ignition—in the open air if possible—so a cartridge should never be changed in the restaurant, still room or kitchen, for example. If a spare lamp, fitted with a full gas cartridge, is kept there should not be a problem with running out of gas in the middle of service.
2. Staff required to change LPG cartridges should be adequately trained in their safe use.
3. LPG-fuelled flambé lamps should be serviced at least once a year.

Barstaff are 'on show' nearly all the time. This is why working behind a bar has been compared with being an actor on the stage. The customer sees and notices everything, from how clean the toilets are to the way staff are dressed, how they pour the drinks and wash the glasses.

If staff slip up on points of hygiene or safety, there is no way of hiding this from the customers. For instance, if the glass the customer is about to drink from has finger marks or the remains of someone else's lipstick on the rim. In this example most customers will refuse to accept the drink. This will be embarrassing to the staff and bad for business, especially if the complaint is overheard by other drinkers at the bar.

Low standards of safety and hygiene put the health of customers and colleagues at risk. Accidents and sickness are more likely to happen in places where staff pay scant attention to their personal habits, and to the cleanliness and tidiness of the premises, and to how they use equipment.

Understanding the effects of alcohol

Places where alcohol is served, such as pubs, wine and cocktail bars, clubs, leisure centres and discotheques have to be extra careful because of the intoxicating effects alcohol can have on people. Someone who has been drinking will react differently to someone who is completely sober, and there are certain activities, driving a car for instance, which become positively dangerous if done by anyone who is under the influence of drink. Some people become very abusive and even violent towards people, others become a danger to themselves because, while drunk, they are not capable of looking after themselves.

This is why the sale of alcohol is carefully controlled. When bars can sell alcohol, to whom, and what kind of alcohol can be sold, are all limited by law. If licensed traders, and staff, do not stick to these rules they can be prosecuted.

Not only can alcohol affect people's judgement and safety in the immediate term, but also, if abused long-term, it can ruin their health, and social and family life. While staff cannot be responsible for making decisions for all customers on what and how much is safe to drink, staff should be aware that, in some circumstances, drink can be dangerous and there comes a time when it is better to stop serving a customer at risk. A licensee has the right to refuse to serve a person for whatever reason, and can get anyone, say a persistent drinker who becomes violent or anti-social in any way, banned from the premises.

Staff should remember that they too are affected by alcohol in the same way as customers. If they drink while working their judgement will be affected.

Emergencies

Barstaff should know what their role is in case of an emergency such as a fire or violence on the premises (see units 22 and 26). Every establishment should have adequate fire fighting equipment, and staff should make sure they find out how to use it before a fire breaks out. Large establishments in particular need to have a well-rehearsed evacuation procedure.

MASTERCRAFT

See *Barcraft: Bar and Alcoholic Beverage Service* and *Barcraft* videos *Thrown in the Deep End* and *A Good Performance*.

!! REMEMBER

Although many people think drinking makes them happy and lively, alcohol is in fact not a stimulant but a depressant. It slows down certain brain functions, affecting judgement, self-control, and skills such as driving and operating machinery. Unfortunately the more people drink the more they think they are capable of, when the truth is that they become less able.

Facts and figures

Research has shown that people who have drunk between one and three pints of beer have more accidents than those who have drunk less than one pint.
One in three drivers killed in traffic accidents in the UK are over the legal limit.
One in five men admitted to hospital in the UK are there for drink-related problems.
Alcohol abuse costs Britain £5 million a day through accidents, sickness and crime.
Nearly half of all fatal road accidents to young people are alcohol related.
Over a third of road traffic accidents to pedestrians are alcohol related.
Over half of deaths from fire and nearly a third of deaths by drowning are alcohol related.

Hygiene and safety checklist for barstaff

Make sure cutlery, crockery and glasses are washed properly in hot water with detergent at 60°C (140°F) and then sterilised in very hot water at 80°C (180°F).

Always hold glasses by the stem or base, plates by the rim, and cups by the handle.

Never allow the nozzle of a drinks dispenser to touch the inside of the glass or come into contact with the drink as it is poured into the glass.

Use a fresh glass for every drink ordered.

Scoop out ice cubes with a non-breakable plastic or metal container, scoop or tongs, never with a glass.

Collect waste regularly and place in easily cleanable containers in a safe place.

Empty ashtrays into a special metal container which will not catch fire.

Always follow the establishment's procedure and/or manufacturer's instructions when carrying out a task and using equipment.

Clear the public areas frequently of glasses, nut and crisp packets, cigarette ends, spills and other debris.

Place tables and chairs so that they will not cause an obstruction.

Report any faulty equipment, furniture and flooring to management.

Make sure open fires are covered by a safety guard.

Wash toilets frequently, replenish towels, soap and toilet rolls, and dispose of any rubbish hygienically.

Watch out for chewing gum stuck under chairs, tables and counter ledges.

Floor areas should be kept clean and dry at all times.

Spills should be wiped clean immediately they occur.

Practise sanitary personal habits: do not smoke, eat, chew, or scratch your head behind the bar. Avoid sneezing, coughing and blowing your nose in food and drink areas. Always wash your hands thoroughly after going to the toilet, smoking, eating or doing any cleaning tasks.

Care of glasses

Glasses need to be washed and handled carefully. If mishandled they can easily break, crack or chip, causing injury, and if not kept clean they will harbour bacteria.

- Avoid collecting glasses in clusters or stacking them (unless they are specially made for stacking), because they will break or crack.
- Avoid subjecting glasses to sudden changes of temperature, for example, pouring in hot liquid, or emptying out ice and then immediately plunging them into hot washing up water or putting in the glass washing machine. Let the glasses stand for a few minutes first to reach room temperature.
- Remove chipped, cracked or broken glasses from service and dispose of them safely, for instance, wrapped in several layers of newspaper or in a special container. Broken glass will quickly cut through plastic bin liners and cut anyone who handles the rubbish.
- Make sure plenty of glasses are available so that washing up does not have to be done in a rush, which could cause injury.
- Carry glasses by the stem, handle or base, never by the rim or with the fingers inside.
- Collect used glasses regularly from all areas.
- If washing glasses by machine always follow the manufacturer's instructions, and make sure equipment is regularly maintained and cleaned.
- If washing glasses by hand, never put more than one glass in the water at any one time, to avoid breakages and injury to the hands.
- Never dry glasses after they have been washed and rinsed: leave them to dry, and then polish with a clean cloth if necessary.
- Store glasses upside down to keep the bowls free from bacteria and dust.
- Never use a glass to scoop up ice or to store cutlery.

 TO DO

Go into a bar of your choice, and take note of how staff treat the glasses. Where and how are they stored before use? How often do staff come to collect used glasses, and how do they carry them away? What system is used for washing and drying them? Were you served with a clean glass for every drink you ordered, and was the glass really clean? List the areas where improvement could be made.

One of the main reasons for cleaning is to remove harmful bacteria. Since bacteria are too small to be seen without a microscope, a lot of attention has to be paid to the way cleaning is done. Visual checks are not enough, because a surface which looks clean could still harbour germs.

Cleaning procedures are designed to remove soil—soil contains food which bacteria need to survive—and to leave surfaces dry—bacteria also need moisture to survive. It is vital that cleaning procedures do not merely transfer soil (and bacteria) from one surface to another. This means:

- maintaining good personal hygiene
- cleaning equipment, including cloths, thoroughly after use, and allowing it to dry where appropriate
- cleaning high risk items such as toilets, baths, wash hand basins, food and drink preparation equipment and surfaces with cleaning equipment reserved for that particular purpose. Colour coding of equipment can help ensure this—for example red cloths for toilets, yellow cloths for baths and wash hand basins, and green for general-purpose use.

Precautions against AIDS

The condition AIDS has led to many deaths throughout the world, and several thousand people in the UK are known to be HIV positive, which means they can pass on the AIDS virus. AIDS is a relatively new and fatal disease for which there is no known cure, and as such is a very serious public health hazard. All hotel and catering staff need to know the dangers and be familiar with the precautions.

AIDS stands for Acquired Immune Deficiency Syndrome; it is caused by a virus known as HIV, which can break down the body's resistance to infections, with the result that the sufferer will eventually die from his or her illness.

In the majority of known cases AIDS has been passed from one person to another through sexual intercourse, or by taking infected blood into the bloodstream, for instance, when drug addicts inject with shared needles, or a blood donor is infected. This is because the virus is carried in the body fluids, particularly semen and blood.

Anyone can contract AIDS. It is not an illness confined to drug addicts, those needing blood transfusions, or homosexuals.

AIDS cannot be transmitted in food and drink, nor can it be passed on by shaking hands.

It is often impossible to tell whether a person has AIDS or is HIV positive because symptoms take several years to appear. So staff need to take special care when handling or cleaning anything that might have had contact with any other person's blood or semen such as razors, used razor blades, hypodermic needles, sanitary towels, soiled sheets and towels, vomit or excreta.

1. Wear gloves when handling items or cleaning surfaces that might be contaminated.
2. Dispose of any sharp objects in a metal or plastic bin which they cannot cut through.
3. Ensure adequate towels are available so that they do not have to be used by more than one person.
4. Dispose of or sterilise cleaning equipment used to clean spills of blood and vomit. If in doubt, check with your supervisor.
5. In some cases it is appropriate to use a chemical disinfectant such as bleach after cleaning surfaces and equipment. Check with your supervisor.

MASTERCRAFT

See *Housecraft: Accommodation Operations, Housecraft: Operations Workbook* and the *Housecraft* video *A Key to Operations.*

?? HOW TO

Discourage pests

1. Remember clean conditions discourage pests (see units 34 and 35).
2. Report any signs of infestation such as:
   - droppings, gnaw marks, footprints, shredded paper: caused by rats and mice
   - small golden brown grubs with hairy tufts on edges of carpets or linen rooms where blankets are stored: these are the larvae of carpet beetles
   - small holes in furniture: a sign of woodworm
   - holes in blankets which have been stored: caused by moths.
3. Report any defect in the building such as cracks and holes which may encourage infestation.
4. Do not leave food uncovered and take particular care with remains of sweet food that is likely to attract pests such as spilt sugar and jam, or biscuit crumbs. Make sure breakfast and other meal trays are removed promptly from guests' rooms.
5. Remove waste promptly to the disposal area making sure it is securely covered.
6. Keep waste bins tightly covered and rubbish bags closed. Clean waste bins after use.

Precautions against Legionnaires' disease

The bacterium which causes Legionnaires' disease lives in damp, warm conditions. It has been found in large numbers in hot and cold water systems, particularly when the temperature of the water is between 20 and 45°C (68 and 115°F), and in stagnant or very slow moving water. These conditions occur in:

- hot water systems in which the water temperature drops during long pipe runs, or through infrequent use
- cold water tanks which are badly sited or poorly insulated so that the water gets quite warm
- air-conditioning systems which use water to collect the excess heat. The water is then cooled in special towers.

When the water has been contaminated by algae, rust from metal piping and tanks, or scaling has occurred, the bacteria will grow even more rapidly. The *Legionella* bacteria only cause illness if they are inhaled in significant numbers. This might happen by breathing in the fine spray of a contaminated water supply from a shower, fast running tap, whirlpool or spa. The bacteria attach themselves to the inside of the lungs, and after several days the victim is likely to suffer from headaches, muscle pain, feverishness and confusion. Legionnaires' disease can be fatal, especially in elderly and very young people.

Bacteria can be prevented from reaching dangerous levels by regular cleaning of water storage tanks and cooling towers and treating the water with chemical disinfectants. Both require special expertise and the work can be dangerous so this is a job for experts only.

Shower heads should also be dismantled regularly by maintenance or housekeeping staff and thoroughly cleaned and disinfected. This is particularly important if the showers are not used very much because the bacteria may have had time to multiply to dangerous levels.

Safety checklist for housekeeping staff

Place warning signs when cleaning floors.

Load trolleys carefully so items will not fall off and you can see where you are going.

Work tidily at all times. For example when damp-dusting a room, don't clutter the floor with items removed from shelves and other surfaces.

Take care when cleaning a window not to lose your balance.

Open and shut doors carefully. Do not leave cupboard doors open.

Never pile soiled sheets, towels or other linen due to be laundered on the floor of the bedroom or corridor, where they may cause a fall.

Never put clean linen on the floor or any other surface where it may pick up bacteria.

Do not run your hands along surfaces you cannot see without checking first that there are no sharp edges.

Take care when running hot water from taps in bathrooms and service areas—it might be hot enough to scald you.

Never attempt to clean light fittings until they have been turned off sufficiently long to cool down. You could scald yourself and a hot bulb will shatter as soon as it is touched with a damp cloth.

Emergencies

Staff must by law be trained in fire drill and evacuation procedures if they work in an establishment of any size. When people are asleep in bed it is all the more important to be able to alert everyone in good time, to minimise distress, injuries, deaths and damage to property (see units 19 to 22).

Housekeeping staff in hotels, guesthouses, student halls of residence and similar establishments may be the first to discover that the occupant of one of the rooms is seriously ill, perhaps having a heart attack or stroke. An ambulance should always be called at once. The more staff know about first aid and are able to act promptly, the more likely it is that the victim will be saved (see units 50 to 60).

Housekeeping staff may also be the first on the scene if someone has died (see unit 26).

◆ ◆ ◆ TO DO

Design a poster which might be displayed in service areas used by housekeeping staff to remind them of the need for high standards of hygiene.

Front of house, sometimes known as reception or the foyer, is the area used by more people than any other because it is, quite simply, the main entrance to the building. Every customer and guest passes through it during their visit, and almost every member of staff will at some time have reason to come here, or communicate with front of house staff by telephone, in the course of his or her work. In an emergency, front of house is usually the central communication point, often with a direct link to the police, fire brigade and ambulance.

So front of house staff need to be especially aware of what is going on throughout the establishment. They need to know what their role is in the event of a fire or bomb alert, for instance, because prompt action of the right kind may save a life. They also need to develop the instincts of a detective—to become aware of the comings and goings, to recognise faces, to have a good memory, to have a nose for suspicious circumstances, to be good at communicating with people. Without these skills, the health and safety of everyone in the establishment could be put at risk.

MASTERCRAFT

See *Guestcraft: Front of House Operations* and *Guestcraft* video *A Good Reception*.

Why front of house must be kept clean and tidy

Because so many people pass through the foyer, or reception, the area is inclined to get more soiled and untidy than other parts of the establishment. For instance, dust gets blown in from outside, people's dirty footprints are left on floors and carpets, sticky fingermarks on furniture and fittings, and items are left lying around or furniture moved so that it causes an obstruction.

The reception area is the 'shop window' of the establishment, where customers form their first impressions, and so it is important to keep it clean and tidy. But dirt and clutter are unhygienic and can be dangerous as well. A child's toy carelessly forgotten in a badly lit hallway can mean an elderly person's broken leg. A loose carpet tack which finds its way into a toddler's mouth can mean an emergency visit to the hospital.

Who goes there?

It is easier for thieves, prostitutes, drug pushers, drunkards, muggers, rapists and terrorists to enter some establishments than others. The difference lies in the security systems practised by management, and in the design of the building itself. People who set out to break the law or create a nuisance soon learn where they can achieve this without being found out and penalised.

Establishments must therefore have a fool-proof system to deter people who are a danger or nuisance to others. It is up to staff, particularly those in the reception area, to keep an eye out for any suspicious circumstances (see units 23 to 27). If staff make an effort to know their guests and customers by name and face, then they will know who they need to challenge in order to find out what their business is. The approach should never be aggressive; the person may have a perfectly legitimate reason for being on the premises. A polite 'May I help you?' will usually do the trick, and if staff are still suspicious, they should inform the person in charge immediately.

Safety and security checklist for front of house staff

Be clean and tidy, and practise hygienic personal habits.
Look out for suspicious circumstances.
Keep the reception area clean, tidy and free of obstructions.

Know what to do in the event of a fire (see units 20 to 22).

Know what to do in the event of a bomb alert (see unit 26).

Know what the law and the establishment requires of you to protect everyone using the premises.

Be discreet. Remember you can be overheard in a public area such as the foyer. Watch what you say to colleagues and customers, even over the phone. It is not good practice inadvertently to announce your establishment's diary of events or to disclose the comings and goings or room numbers of customers. Unscrupulous people may take advantage.

Remember it is not just unauthorised people on the premises who can be a security risk. Customers and staff have also been known to steal, become violent, or create a nuisance in some way. Staff have a duty to report anyone, even their own colleagues, if they have strong reason to suspect that anything untoward is going on.

▶ ▶ ▶ TO DO

Take a man who has deliberately stationed himself in the reception area of the hotel in order to hear any information he can take advantage of. He is a thief. As luck would have it, he overhears the telephone exchange in which the reservation for the coach party of 50 is made. He now knows that the group is due to arrive at 5 o'clock the next afternoon. So, next day, he hangs around outside to make sure he enters the reception area along with the 50 other people, pretty sure that no one will become suspicious of him among all those faces. He can hardly believe his luck: all those suitcases standing unattended in the foyer! And he makes sure he listens very carefully as a member of staff gives out keys, stating clearly the guest's name and then the number of the room allocated. As far as the thief is concerned, this hotel is a winner. Once he has picked up what he can now, he will definitely be paying a return visit to an establishment with such lax security.

Discuss with one or more colleagues the points where front of house staff were at fault in causing this breach of security. How else could the thief turn the information he has gained to his advantage? List the ways in which front of house staff could have improved their security procedures to make things more difficult for the thief. Finally, role play a similar situation, relevant to your workplace or the subjects you are studying, where a thief takes advantage of breaches of security in front of house. Take care to pin point during the role play the exact moments when security is lax. Then discuss with your group where staff could have improved their security procedures.

✳ FOR INTEREST

Many establishments which provide overnight accommodation no longer display customers' keys, room numbers and pigeon holes on a rack at the back of the reception desk, where they are tell-tale signs to any thief. A key on the hook of room 114, for instance, is an indication that the occupant is out, and if there is a message in the accompanying pigeon hole, then any self-respecting thief knows almost for sure that it is safe to break into that room. A particularly cheeky thief who knows the establishment's security system to be lax may even impersonate the occupant, and be handed the key unchallenged, on a plate as it were!

Put those skills to the test

The real test of whether a security system is working happens when there is extra pressure on an establishment's resources.

Say, a booking for overnight accommodation is made at a hotel for a coach party of 50. The reservation will be made through front of house staff, who will, as usual inform the housekeeping department that a certain number of rooms are required for a certain number of nights, so that these can be prepared. The kitchen and restaurant will also be notified so that adequate catering arrangements can be made, with extra staff on if necessary.

A party of 50 all arriving at the same time means that the front of house staff will also have to be ready: to welcome and register them, allocate rooms promptly and ensure items of luggage are safely delivered.

All this takes planning. If front of house staff fail to inform the right people within their own department and in other departments, then tasks which involve hygiene, safety and security will be skimped through lack of time and staff or, worse still, not done at all, putting at risk the welfare of everyone—customers and staff alike.

Food and drink items must be stored correctly as soon as they arrive at the establishment so that they are in good condition when they reach the customers. Storage areas should be kept clean, tidy and well-ventilated to prevent the build up of bacteria. If items are stored incorrectly they will lose flavour and colour, and worse still could cause food poisoning.

On delivery

Correct storage begins before the product reaches the catering establishment, and it is up to staff to make sure that goods delivered are up to standard before accepting them.

1. Damaged or discoloured cans, cartons, bottles and other containers should not be accepted, and the entire consignment should be carefully examined before any of it is received. The 'sell-by' dates should also be checked on each item to make sure that the stock is not too old to sell.
2. In order to keep track of goods coming in and going out (this is called stock control) it is important at the delivery stage to know exactly what has been received. The delivery note or invoice from the suppliers should not be signed until the member of staff receiving the goods is satisfied that it tallies with what has actually been delivered and with the original order. If there are any shortages or discrepancies, these should be reported to the delivery person and stated on the delivery note or invoice so that the matter can be put right by the suppliers later. If this is not done at the point of delivery, it will be impossible to track down how the shortages or discrepancies occurred. One of the important functions of stock control is to prevent pilfering and to find out quickly if anything dishonest has occurred.
3. Raw foods, especially meat and fish, and strong smelling items such as cheese, onions and garlic, should be kept separately from other items to avoid contamination.
4. Once unloaded, goods should be clearly marked with the date of delivery to ensure that they are used in strict rotation, the older items first. It is useful to know the date of delivery in case there is any complaint later.
5. Store all items in their correct place, making sure that they are securely under lock and key where possible, to avoid thefts.

The law is explicit in stating that any food consisting of meat, fish, gravy or imitation cream, or prepared from or containing any of these substances, or any egg or milk, must be stored at a temperature of below 10°C (50°F) or above 63°C (145°F) unless the food is intended for immediate consumption (see unit 16).

This does not apply to bread, biscuits, cakes, chocolate, dried, canned or bottled foods, unplucked game or poultry and similar items which are not as vulnerable to harmful microorganisms (see units 38 and 39).

Storage areas depend on the type of food or drink and how it is prepared and packaged. Each kind of storage has a different temperature and environment suited to certain foods and drink

Refrigerators and freezers should be defrosted regularly, cleaned with detergent and hot water, and then rinsed with clean water and thoroughly dried. Walk in freezers and cold stores/rooms should be washed out weekly, and cleared of debris as it accumulates

---

‼ REMEMBER

It is not possible to calculate the shelf life of an item without knowing its history. This is why the 'sell by' date stamped on packaged food is so useful, because it provides an immediate indicator of the freshness of the food. The shelf life of an item varies depending not only on what kind of food it is, but also on the way it was first packaged, and the temperature at which it is subsequently stored.

▶ ▶ ▶ TO DO

Find out how the establishment where you work or study, or a catering establishment of your choice, organises its stock rotation. If the establishment serves food, how are canned goods, raw meats, fresh fruits and vegetables controlled on the 'first in, first out' basis? If the establishment is a pub or another kind of bar, how is the rotation of beers, lagers, crisps and nuts, and tobacco controlled?

Storage checklist

Storerooms and store cupboards should be secure from pests (see units 34 and 35).

They should only be open to authorised staff.

They should be organised so that both incoming and outgoing orders can be easily checked, weighed or counted.

Spillages, which attract bacteria and pests, and can cause accidents, should be cleared up immediately.

A good stock rotation system should be used so that so that the 'first in first out' rule can be applied. Rotation of stock avoids wastage and potential danger to health.

Items should be stacked safely so there is no danger of tins rolling off shelves or piles collapsing.

Heavy items should be stored on the lower levels to make handling easier.

Items should be stacked so that stock counting is quick and straightforward – no part-filled boxes, no hidden items, all like-items together.

All poisonous substances should be stored in clearly labelled containers, well away from food areas, to avoid confusion.

Beers, such as real ales, which are still 'live' when they reach the establishment, that is the fermentation process is not yet completed, require very careful storage in the cellar so that they do not spoil. It is essential to keep the temperature exactly right, and to make sure that the cellar, cask bungs and taps, bar dispense taps and beer lines (pipes which bring the beer up from the cellar to the bar) are kept scrupulously clean.

Bottles of wine should be stored on their side so the cork does not dry out.

Raw food, especially meat and poultry, should always be stored away from cooked food, ideally in separately refrigerators or freezers.

Raw meats should never be allowed to drip through to food on lower shelves of the refrigerator.

Foods should be protected to keep pests, dust and other foreign substances out and to prevent drying out, cross-contamination, and absorption of smells.

Refrigerators should not be overcrowded, nor should food be placed directly in front of the cooling unit as this reduces air circulation.

Food from partly-used cans should be transferred to a suitable clean container and covered before being stored in the refrigerator.

Never leave refrigerator and freezer doors open when they are in use.

If for any reason ice cream is allowed to melt, it should never be re-frozen and eaten. It should be discarded immediately, since bacteria will almost certainly have attacked it.

Fruit and vegetables should be regularly examined for mould and other spoilage which will spread to fresh food unless disposed of immediately. Plastic wrapping, such as cling film, should be removed to avoid condensation which spoils the food.

Flour and other cereals should be stored in bins above ground level to avoid damp, and to discourage pests.

Storage	Temperature °C	°F	Type of food stored
dry food stores	10 to 15	50 to 60	flour and other cereals, biscuits, canned fruit and vegetables
	7 to 10	45 to 50	canned/bottled drinks
cellars	11 to 15	52 to 60	cask-conditioned beers (real ale), keg beers and lager (usually kept in special cold rooms), wines
cold stores/rooms	3 to 4	36 to 39	fresh vegetables, milk, cheese, butter, canned and bottled drinks, including beers and lagers, foods being cooled, such as freshly cooked chicken, before being stored in refrigerator
refrigerators	1 to 4	34 to 39	dairy products such as cream, yogurt, soft cheeses, milk, cakes and pastries containing cream and custard, eggs, mayonnaise, cans of pasteurised ham, cooked meats
	1 to −1	30 to 34	fresh meat and poultry
	0 to −2	28 to 32	fresh fish
freezers	−18 to −21	0 to −6	pre-frozen food, ice-cream

✱ FOR INTEREST

Minimum storage temperatures for certain foods will be reduced in new food hygiene regulations due in late 1989/early 1990.

below 5°C (41°F)
alkaline soft cheeses which have been cut up or sliced from the whole cheese, products which have been prepared for consumption without further cooking or reheating including meat, meat substitute, fish, egg and dairy products and vegetables, smoked or otherwise cured fish and smoked or otherwise cured sliced meat which has not been preserved so it will keep at room temperature.

below 8°C (46°F)
whole soft cheeses, yogurt, prepared vegetable salad, cooked food which will be reheated (meat, meat substitute, fish, egg, dairy, vegetables), sandwiches, uncooked dough.

An increasingly sophisticated range of leisure facilities is available at health clubs, sports centres, hotels and holiday centres. These include swimming pools, spa pools, solariums, steam rooms, jacuzzis, massage showers, gymnasiums, mini-gyms, fitness rooms, and squash courts. The leisure area often has a relaxation room or lounge, bars and restaurants, as well as beauty, massage and hairdressing facilities.

Many leisure activities, such as swimming, squash and fitness training, are potentially hazardous, and specially trained staff need to be on duty at all times, able to give first aid treatment if necessary. All pools must have staff qualified as life savers.

Cleaning leisure areas

Most of the floors, wall surfaces and fittings in leisure centres and other premises containing leisure facilities are designed to withstand the humid conditions and heavy use. Surfaces should be easy to clean, with no nooks and crannies to harbour bacteria. For instance, carpets are no use in areas near swimming pools because they would get waterlogged, thus encouraging the growth of bacteria. Non-porous materials, able to take frequent cleaning such as ceramic tiles, concrete, plastic and lino are much more hygienic. If used for flooring they should also be non-slip.

Furniture also needs to be made from materials which will withstand frequent cleaning and humid conditions. Strong, light materials such as steel or cast aluminium are often given a non-corrosive coating which protects the metal. If this coating gets chipped or damaged in any way, the matter should be reported to prevent rust or other corrosion setting in.

Security

There are two aspects to security in leisure areas.

1. Protecting the safety of the users. This may mean keeping out anyone who is not authorised to be in the area. In a health club, members may be asked to produce their membership cards, or in a hotel the guests may be asked to give their name and room number. Every establishment has its own rules which should be respected by everyone using the facilities. Management have the right to refuse admission to anyone who may be a threat to the safety of other people or to themselves. For instance, most health clubs have a minimum age limit for members because potentially dangerous equipment is provided.
2. Protecting the safety of the users' property. Lockers are usually provided for valuables, but in some leisure centres clothes are left in changing rooms. Any problems with lockers should be reported, for instance lost keys, or locks which have been tampered with. Staff should be on the look out for anyone who is acting suspiciously so that crime can be prevented.

Maintaining swimming pools

Almost always there will be a team of maintenance staff and trained pool attendants to look after swimming pools, but if conditions go wrong users can suffer gastro-enteritis, dysentry and even typhoid. The problems—made worse by the fact that the water is usually at a perfect temperature for bacteria to breed: 28 to

Safety checklist

- The area should be well-lit to prevent accidents.
- External windows should be kept clean.
- Emergency lights should be tested every day.
- Floors, passages, ramps and stairs should be kept free from obstruction and any substance likely to cause an accident.
- Lifebelts must be in place at all times, ready for use in an emergency.
- Broken or missing tiles and sharp edges on floors where people walk barefoot should be reported immediately.
- Drainage gulleys should be kept clean and unblocked.
- The humidity and presence of chemicals in the air will cause metals to corrode faster than usual. Look out for signs of corrosion in hidden areas especially, such as light fittings and roof voids.
- When using electrical equipment, take care to keep plugs and other electrical connections dry.
- Never attempt to clean up spillages of chemicals used to treat swimming pool or spa water, but report them at once so that they can be cleared up immediately in a safe manner.

If any of the following problems occur it should be reported immediately because it is a danger to health and safety. Each one of them is serious enough for the pool to be closed until the matter is put right:

- unclear water: the bottom of the pool should be clearly visible
- a smell of gas
- users complaining of sore eyes and skin irritations
- no life guards, or below minimum number required, at pool side
- chemicals leaking out of containers.

(It is important that chemicals are kept in their proper storage area and in containers which are clearly labelled as to their contents.)

30°C (82 to 86°F)—are caused when substances which attract bacteria are present in high concentrations:

- sweat, body fats and oils and make-up present on the bodies of users even though they do shower before they enter the water
- urine introduced by thoughtless users
- dust and grit, litter, cigarette ends, insects, leaves and grass cuttings (with outdoor pools) which get blown into the water.

Indoor pools rarely need a complete change of water, but outdoor swimming pools will need draining and thorough cleaning once a year. Normal filtering systems change the water gradually, though some effectively renew it every 4 to 6 hours. Regular cleaning tasks include:

- removing any floating debris from the surface, normally with a hand-held filter, though some pools have a special skimming device at water level to do the job
- cleaning off any build-up of body fats on the water line, using special pastes or powders and a nylon scouring pad
- cleaning the bottom of the pool by sucking up water and debris through a hose linked to the pumping system
- using chemical disinfectants to kill any bacteria in the water (the level of disinfectant should be tested every two hours or so with a special testing kit)
- maintaining the correct pH value of the water (level of its acidity and alkaline content), which should be checked every two hours or so using a special device)
- filtering the water through sand to trap such foreign bodies as hair, skin flakes and algae, and then through a flocculent agent which forms a gel to trap remaining particles.

Cleaning chemicals used

Care must be taken that the correct chemical is used in the recommended concentration to avoid irritation to the skin and eyes. If wrongly used some chemicals release dangerous gases. Disinfectants include chlorine, bromine and ozone. Algicides are often added about once a week to keep algae (a type of plant) from growing.

▶ ▶ ▶ TO DO

The Health and Safety Commission and the Sports Council have identified the major causes of accidents in swimming pools. Unclear pool water (preventing casualties from being seen) and the absence of, or inadequate response by lifeguards in an emergency are two causes that management action can help prevent. Other causes include:

- people swimming a short time after drinking alcohol or eating a heavy meal
- unruly behaviour such as running on the side of the pool, people ducking other swimmers, performing acrobatics in the water, shouting and screaming (this can distract attention in an emergency)
- poor or inexperienced swimmers straying out of their depth (half of those who drown are aged under 15)
- people diving into insufficient depth of water
- people using pools intended to be out of use
- people who have a medical condition such as epilepsy, asthma, diabetes or a heart condition, not taking sufficient care.

Design a poster which would point out the dangers to swimmers of some of these bad practices.

Supervising swimming pool users

Accidents can occur all too easily at swimming pools. An inexperienced swimmer may get out of depth, panic and drown. A person unfamiliar with the pool may take a deep dive, hit the bottom and get a serious head or spine injury. An over-strenuous swimmer may have a heart attack. Someone who goes swimming too soon after a meal may get severe cramp and be unable to swim to safety.

Accidents can also occur as a result of over-crowding or rowdy behaviour. Poor maintenance and cleaning of the pool may result in cloudy water making it difficult to see swimmers in distress, or a dangerous level of chemicals in the water (see previous unit). Missing or damaged life belts and faulty poolside alarms may mean the difference between a misadventure and serious injury or death.

Some measure of supervision is necessary at any swimming pool. What form this takes will depend on what controls there are over who uses the pool, the experience and age of the swimmers, how many are likely to use the pool at one time, and on what the pool is being used for—general leisure activities, for example, or competitive training. The following measures should be considered by the operator.

Encouraging responsible behaviour   Safety signs, posters, explanatory leaflets, and advice from pool attendants are some of the methods that can be used to inform swimming pool users of the hazards and to encourage them to behave responsibly.

Controlling access to the pool   The pool or its surrounding area should not become so over-crowded that people are at risk. Management should set the maximum number to take account of how the pool is used. For example a shallow paddling pool for children and their parents can take more people than a deep pool which is used for diving or swimming training.

Controlling use of the pool   Some leisure centres reserve the pool at certain times of the day for specific uses, for instance school children in the afternoons, members of the swimming club in the mornings.

If the pool is loaned to outside organisations the owners still have a responsibility for the safety of the people using it (see unit 12). Arrangements for supervising the swimmers should be agreed in advance with the hirers and in writing. It may still be advisable for the owner to have a trained member of staff on duty.

Providing trained pool attendants   Pools open to the public are supervised at all times by qualified lifeguards. Constant supervision should also be provided if:

- the pool is used by unaccompanied children aged under 15
- crowded conditions are expected, for example a hot bank holiday weekend
- food or alcohol is available to pool users
- activities are taking place which are likely to generate excitement, such as disco-swimming.

Constant supervision may not be necessary if the pool is quite small, used by a limited number of people, those people are likely to behave responsibly and there is no diving or other poolside facility which poses a particular risk.

At times when the poolside supervision is not provided a member of staff should be on-call to deal with any emergency. That person should be trained in rescue, resuscitation and first aid.

Emergency equipment at the poolside
- An alarm or telephone to summon help.
- Lifebelts, poles and similar equipment to support swimmers in distress or help them reach safety.
- A notice explaining how to get help in an emergency.

▶ ▶ ▶ **TO DO**

Visit two swimming pools in your area, if possible one which is open to the general public and one which is for the use of hotel guests or club members only. Note and compare the safety measures provided at each and identify any additional safety measure you think should be provided.

Duties of lifeguards

- To keep all areas of the pool and all the pool users under constant supervision. A trained lifeguard will spot the difference between someone who is shouting and splashing for fun and a person in difficulty.
- To carry out rescues and take emergency action as required.
- To give emergency first aid.
- To give effective resuscitation.
- To communicate effectively with swimming pool users and with any other lifeguards on duty.
- To check safety and rescue equipment and report any incidents which may require improved safety arrangements.

If a person is likely to be using the pool at a time when no one else is around, for instance an early-rising hotel guest, then there should be some system to ensure that the management know who is using the pool at any given time. One method might be to ask anyone using the pool in such conditions to notify the hotel reception

> Lifeguards should carry whistles to summon attention and wear distinctive clothing or special identification so they can be immediately recognised for who they are.
>
> Their duties should be organised so that they can maintain a high level of vigilance. Regular breaks are important and a variety of duties can prevent boredom.
>
> Guidelines published in *Safety in Swimming Pools* by the Health and Safety Commission and the Sports Council (on which this text is based) recommend that at least one lifeguard is provided for pools over 170 square metres (200 square yards) in size and two for pools over 312 square metres (370 square yards) in size (with proportionate increases thereafter).
>
> More lifeguards should be provided if the pool is busy, or food and alcohol is provided at the poolside. The number of lifeguards should also be increased if the pool has separate or hidden areas, if it is unusually deep, or if diving or other special equipment is provided.

Spas

Spas need very careful maintenance by experts to ensure they are pleasant and safe to be in. Filtration methods and chemicals are similar to those used for swimming pools, however cleaning has to be even more thorough.

- Spas are used by more people at any one time than swimming pools so there is a higher concentration of body oils, skin flakes and other organic wastes to be filtered out.
- They are kept at a high temperature so the water evaporates more quickly and has to be constantly topped up.
- The rapid circulation and relatively high temperatures of the water reduce the effectiveness of disinfectants and increase the chances of bacterial growth.

 FIRST AID

The effect of an injury or illness can be greatly reduced or a life saved if prompt first aid is given.

First aid is the initial emergency treatment given to a casualty following an injury or illness. The casualty is likely to need further attention from a doctor and may have to be sent to hospital in an ambulance.

First aid tides the casualty over the period between the incident happening and further professional help arriving. In many cases prompt first aid will save the person's life, but it is never intended as a complete treatment or cure in itself.

The aims of first aid

- To keep the casualty alive.
- To establish that there is no further danger to the casualty or to yourself.
- To relieve pain and distress.
- To prevent the casualty's condition worsening.
- To help the casualty to recover.

First aiders   A first aider is a trained person who has gained a first aid certificate within the past three years from an approved organisation (see unit 13). Large establishments usually employ one or more first aiders and some large hotels also employ qualified medical staff.

Where no trained first aider is employed, a member of staff should be appointed to take charge if an accident occurs. This person should have some basic knowledge of first aid, and ideally have completed a first aid course run by an organisation such as the Red Cross, St John's or St Andrew's Ambulance Associations.

First aid boxes   The law requires an employer to provide first aid boxes. How many and the content will depend on the number of employees in the workplace (see unit 13).

Accident reports   The law requires that certain accidents at work are recorded in an accident book or on a suitable form and reported (see unit 13). If the injury worsens, or the casualty wishes to make an insurance claim an accident report is essential.

First on the scene

The first priority of first aid is to save lives. This may mean calling for help, removing the casualty from danger and giving first aid treatment. The first person on the scene of an accident should assess the situation, decide what can be done and when help is required. There is a general procedure which should be followed.

1. Do not move the casualty until absolutely necessary
Unless there is any likely danger to the casualty or to yourself, for example from fire, escaping gas, falling masonry or electric shock, do not move the casualty because this can worsen injuries. Leave it to the professionals.
Road traffic accident   Arrange for someone to divert the traffic. Do not attempt to move the casualty unless it is dangerous to leave the person where he or she is.
Electric shock   Break the contact by switching off the current at the wall socket or mains. Do not touch the casualty until the current has been switched off because you will get an electric shock.
Poisonous gas or fumes   If possible cut off the source. Otherwise move the casualty.
Fire or falling masonry   Move the casualty.

▶ ▶ ▶ **TO DO**

Make a list of the contents of a first aid box at your college or workplace. How many first aid boxes are provided? How many students/staff are on the premises?

Alternatively or in addition
Get hold of an accident report form, or photocopy a blank page from an accident report book. Imagine that a colleague has been injured in a hotel, catering, leisure or tourism establishment and fill in the form. Ask your supervisor or tutor to check that you have given sufficient information.

100

2. Take immediate action

- Check that nothing is blocking the casualty's throat or the rest of the airway (see unit 54).
- Check the casualty is breathing (see unit 54).
- Check the casualty's heart is beating (see unit 55).
- Check for any severe bleeding and control it (see unit 56).
- If the casualty is unconscious, but breathing normally, place him or her in the recovery position (see unit 52).
- If the casualty has stopped breathing, give mouth-to-mouth resuscitation (see unit 54).
- If the casualty has stopped breathing and the heart has stopped beating, give external chest compression (see unit 55).

3. Telephone for help

Get professional help as soon as possible. If there are many casualties this should be done before attempting to give first aid.

If a casualty has stopped breathing or his or her heart has stopped beating, give first aid treatment before phoning for assistance. If possible get someone else to phone.

1. Use the nearest telephone.
2. Dial 999. No money is required.
3. Ask for the necessary service: ambulance, fire brigade or police.
4. When you get through, give the number of the telephone you are calling from so that the operator can call you back if necessary.
5. Give the location of the accident.
6. State the nature of the accident or illness, for example fire, heart attack.
7. Give the number of casualties.
8. Give as much detail of the injuries as possible.
9. Remain on the phone until the emergency service operator rings off to be sure that you have given sufficient information.

4. Find out more about the injury or illness

Once necessary emergency first aid is given and the casualty is conscious, get as much information as possible about the injury or illness so that you can pass this on to the doctor or ambulance attendants to help them diagnose the problem.

1. Ask the casualty to describe how he/she feels. Is there any pain, loss of vision, does he/she feel thirsty and so on.
2. If it is a medical problem such as a heart attack, ask the casualty about his or her medical history.
3. Look for obvious signs of injury or illness, including sweating, bleeding, bruising or swelling.
4. Ask witnesses to describe what they saw.

5. Keep the casualty comfortable

Stay calm. Reassure the casualty kindly and confidently. Keep the casualty protected from the cold and relieve pain if possible. It is generally not advisable to give the casualty anything by mouth in case it causes choking. When professional help arrives, give any information that will help diagnosis and hand over responsibility.

 # FIRST AID

With some injuries such as a cut or wound it will be clear what sort of treatment is required, at least in the first instance. In other cases it may not be easy to know what is wrong, for example with internal bleeding or a fractured bone. In yet other cases the first priority will be to restore breathing, for example if the patient is choking, or to try and revive the heart action, then place the casualty in the recovery position.

Knowing what action to take will be helped by an understanding of what can go wrong to a person and what the signs and symptoms are (see units 52 to 59).

Choking

If not relieved, choking can cause unconsciousness very quickly, and, within a short time, death. Children and elderly people are particularly at risk from choking.

Choking occurs when food or drink, or foreign bodies such as beads, become lodged at the back of the throat and obstruct breathing. The casualty may show any of the following signs:

- severe coughing and spluttering (indicating a partially blocked windpipe)
- unable to speak or breathe, and possibly pointing to the throat—do not confuse choking with a heart attack, where the casualty can speak and breathe (see unit 57)
- blueness of the lips and mouth
- congestion of the face and neck, with veins becoming prominent
- loss of consciousness.

If choking appears to be minor
Advise the casualty to breathe slowly and deeply to relax the throat muscles and clear the windpipe. The casualty's own reflexes will often dislodge the blockage.

If the casualty is conscious and standing or sitting
1. Do not waste time asking an adult casualty to move into a different position. If the casualty is a small child or baby, sit yourself down and lie the person over your knees, head down.
2. Remove any debris or false teeth from the mouth. Use your fingers to hook out obstacles, but be very careful, especially with children, not to make the blockage worse.
3. Tell the casualty to cough.
4. If coughing does not help, tell the casualty to bend over so the head is lower than the lungs. If the casualty is standing, help him or her bend over your forearm.
5. With the heel of one hand, slap the casualty sharply on the back between the shoulder blades up to four times. Use a light slap for young children and only very light pressure for a baby.
6. Check if the obstruction is dislodged and if necessary remove it from the mouth. If not, use the abdominal thrust method (also called the Heimlich method) to squeeze the remaining air out of the lungs and so dislodge the object (see HOW TO box).

If the casualty is conscious and lying down
1. Roll the casualty on to one side, facing you and resting against your body. If the casualty is lying on the floor you should kneel beside him or her.
2. Proceed as for step 5 onwards (as above).

!! **REMEMBER**
- Prompt and expert first aid will save lives.
- Familiarise yourself with a first aid manual, for example the authorised manual of St John Ambulance, St Andrew's Ambulance Association and the British Red Cross Society.
- If possible, go on a first aid course and get the chance to practise the different techniques under the guidance of an experienced and qualified first-aider.

TO DO
Find out the details of the first aid courses in your area. How long do they last? What qualifications do they lead to? How much do they cost? Decide, with the help of your tutor or supervisor, if one would be suitable for you to go on and how you could arrange to attend.

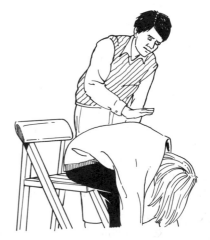

If the casualty is unconscious

1. Turn the casualty on to the back, clear the airway and start mouth-to-mouth resuscitation (see unit 54). You may be able to blow past the obstruction and so revive the casualty for treatment as above.
2. If this does not work, turn the casualty on to one side, with the head well back and give four sharp slaps on the back (as above).
3. If you are still not successful, use the abdominal thrust method.
4. If this does not work give mouth-to-mouth resuscitation again.
5. Once the obstacle has been removed place the casualty in the recovery position (see unit 52) and call for medical help.

Fainting

Fainting is a sudden and momentary loss of consciousness caused by a temporary lack of blood to the brain. This may be due to emotional upset, exhaustion, a hot stuffy atmosphere, lack of food, or standing for long periods.

The person will feel giddy and uneasy, look very pale, the skin may feel cold and there might be cold sweat on the skin. The pulse will be slow at first and quite weak (see unit 55).

If the person can be helped as soon as any of these signs become apparent: help him or her to sit down and lean forward with the head well down. If the person is in a crowd, for example, and there is no where to sit down, encourage him or her to flex the leg muscles and move the toes. Both these steps help restore normal blood circulation. If the person has fainted:

1. Lie the casualty down on his or her back, raising the legs on a cushion or folded clothes for example. This will help the flow of blood to the head. Put the head in the open airway position (see unit 54).
2. Ensure there is a good supply of fresh, cool air. Fanning the face gently will help if there is no breeze.
3. Loosen any tight clothing.
4. As the casualty regains consciousness give help to sit up and quiet reassurance.
5. Check the pulse and breathing rates regularly until the casualty is fully recovered (see units 54 and 55). Do not give anything to drink until the casualty is fully conscious—sips of cold water at this stage may help. Do not give the casualty any alcohol.
6. If the casualty does not regain consciousness, give resuscitation (see units 54 and 55).

??   **HOW TO**

Use the abdominal thrust method (for severe choking)

Note: this method may damage some of the casualty's internal organs, so it should only be used when other methods have failed (see main text).

If the casualty is conscious
1. Stand or kneel behind the casualty.
2. Place your closed fist against the abdomen just below the rib cage with the thumb upwards.

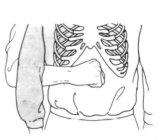

3. Grasp your fist with your other hand. Then press sharply and suddenly into the casualty's abdomen with a quick upward thrust. Repeat up to four times if necessary

If the casualty is unconscious
1. Lie the casualty on his or her back with the head in the open airway position (see unit 54) and kneel astride the body (or if necessary to one side).

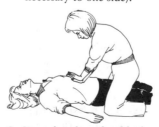

2. Place the heel of one hand in the centre of the casualty's upper abdomen (just below the rib cage). Place your other hand on top of this (palm down as before). Keep your fingers straight.

3. Press sharply and suddenly into the abdomen with a quick upward thrust. Repeat up to four times if necessary.

Unconsciousness

When unconscious casualties are breathing satisfactorily and their hearts are beating, they should be turned as quickly as possible on to their stomachs and arranged in the recovery position (also called unconscious position). See HOW TO box. This position keeps the airway open by:

- preventing the casualty's tongue from dropping to the back of the throat
- allowing fluid such as vomit or blood to drain from the mouth
- keeping the air passage in a wide open position (as the neck and head are in an extended position).

The recovery position is a life-saver and usually has priority over other treatment. But take great care in moving the casualty, especially if there are any serious wounds. And if you think the casualty may have a fractured spine or neck, do not attempt to move him or her until help arrives. There are special techniques for dealing with suspected spinal injuries.

ABC, the vital needs for any casualty:

A an open *airway*
B adequate *breathing*
C sufficient *circulation*

!! **REMEMBER**

A casualty should be treated as unconscious unless fully alert or able to be roused easily.

Asphyxia

Asphyxia occurs when insufficient oxygen reaches the heart and hence the body tissues. It can kill very quickly. The causes include choking, suffocation, hanging, strangulation or throttling, drowning, injury to the chest wall and lungs, electrocution or electric shock, poisoning and stroke. The signs generally include one or more of the following:

- difficulty in breathing, possibly noisy or gurgling
- frothing at the mouth
- blue lips and fingertips
- confusion
- unconsciousness
- breathing stops.

1. Remove the cause or help the casualty away from whatever has caused the asphyxiation.
2. Ensure a supply of fresh air.

If the casualty is unconscious
3. Open the airway (see unit 54).
4. Give mouth-to-mouth resuscitation and external chest compression as necessary (see units 54 and 55).
5. When the casualty is breathing normally, place in recovery position (see unit 52). Check regularly on breathing, pulse rate and levels of consciousness (see units 51, 54 and 55). Call for medical help immediately.

Drowning
Get air into the casualty's lungs as soon as possible. In shallow water, support him or her with your hands and give mouth-to-mouth resuscitation. If the casualty is in deep water, give the occasional breath of air while you bring him or her to dry land.

Once you have restored breathing and put the casualty in the recovery position, keep him or her warm until help arrives. Remove wet clothing if possible and cover with a blanket, dry towel or spare clothing, for example.

Stages of unconsciousness

A person will become unconscious when the normal activity of the brain is interrupted. This may be due to interference with the nervous system and/or blood circulation. There are three stages. The casualty is:

- *drowsy*—easily roused for a few moments, but then passes back into a sleep-like state. During this stage the casualty may be able to answer questions, which would help the doctor later
- in a *stupor*—does not respond to questions, or is unable to understand the question
- in a *coma*—motionless and silent and cannot be roused at all.

A casualty may pass quickly through all three stages or may remain in one. The first-aider should note whether the onset of unconsciousness was sudden or slow to help the doctor in diagnosis later.

▶ ▶ ▶ TO DO

Practise placing a friend in the recovery position. Do this with the help of a qualified first-aider.

?? HOW TO

Place a casualty in the recovery position

1. If the casualty is wearing spectacles, remove them.
2. Kneel close to the casualty.
3. If the casualty is lying on his or her back, the first step is to gently roll the body over:
   - turn the head to face you, and tilt it back with the jaw forward so the airway is kept open (see unit 54)
   - straighten out the arm nearest you, and tuck the hand (open) under the casualty's bottom

   - rest the casualty's other arm on the chest
   - take hold of the casualty's far leg under the knee or ankle and cross it over the leg nearest you
   - with one hand supporting the casualty's head, use the other arm to pull body over on to its side to rest against you.

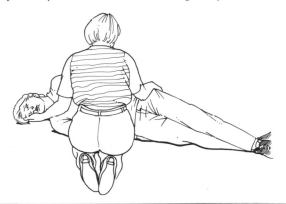

4. Arrange the body so it is lying face to one side with the airway open and the arms and legs arranged so the body will not roll over:
   - one arm should be at right angles to support the upper body
   - one leg should be at right angles to support the lower body
   - the other arm and leg should be lying free of the body and parallel to it, so the circulation is not interfered with.

Epilepsy

This is a disorder of the body's central nervous system. A person suffering from a minor epileptic fit will start to act unusually or strangely, for example staring blankly, smacking the lips. Keep away other people until the fit passes, and protect the person from any dangers.

A minor fit may be followed by a major epileptic attack, but these can also come quite unexpectedly. Major fits generally go through a number of stages. First the person loses consciousness, sometimes letting out a strange cry. Then he or she will become rigid and stop breathing for a few moments. In the next stage the muscles will start jerking or convulsing, sometimes quite violently. Breathing can become more noisy or difficult and there may be frothing around the mouth, bleeding at the mouth (if the tongue has been bitten), loss of bladder or bowel control.

After the convulsions have subsided, the muscles will relax, but it is usually five minutes or so before the person regains consciousness. It can then take up to an hour for the confusion and strange behaviour to pass.

If you are in time to help someone at the start of a major epileptic fit, help them to lie down on their back in as safe a place as possible. Clear away any obstacles and make the person comfortable, loosening tight clothing around the neck and supporting the head with some folded clothes, for example. If the person has already fallen, do not attempt to move or lift him or her. Don't try and restrain the person, or attempt to wake him or her. Never put anything in the person's mouth, or try to open it.

When the convulsions have passed, put the person in the recovery position (see unit 52) to help the breathing. Remain with the person until he or she is fully recovered. But don't give him or her anything to drink unless you are sure that recovery is complete.

Only call an ambulance if the person takes longer than 15 minutes or so to regain consciousness—many epilepsy sufferers carry a card which will say how long they usually take to wake up, or has suffered an injury during the fit, or has a succession of fits one soon after the other.

> ### ▶ ▶ ▶ TO DO
>
> It can be quite frightening seeing someone suffering from an epileptic fit. If people don't understand what is going on they can react in a hard, even cruel way to the sufferer. Because of this general feeling some people who suffer from epileptic fits hardly ever venture out of their home, just in case they should have a fit in the street or a shop, for example.
>
> Go to your library and read up some more information on what causes epilepsy and how sufferers can be helped. If you know any doctors or nurses they will also be able to give you information. Then prepare a short talk which you might give to a group of your colleagues. You want them to become more aware of the difficulties and react in a positive, sympathetic manner if they should encounter someone suffering from an epileptic fit. To add interest to your talk and help you get across the main points, you should prepare some drawings, diagrams or charts which could be made into overhead transparencies.

Diabetes

Diabetes occurs when the body fails to regulate the blood sugar level. Sufferers have to take great care over what they eat and many have to take insulin as an injection or in tablet form two or three times a day. This corrects the sugar balance, but if a diabetic has mistakenly taken too much insulin, or not eaten enough food or has been over active the blood sugar level may become too low. This can affect the brain and lead to unconsciousness and even death. (Too much sugar has the same effect but the problem develops gradually and it is rare for a first-aider to have to deal with such a casualty.)

The early warning signs of an inadequate sugar level can be difficult to notice if the sufferer has been on insulin for a long time. They include:

- dizziness, weakness and lightheadedness
- pale, cold and sweating skin
- mental confusion, possible irrational or aggressive behaviour
- lack of physical coordination and possibly slurred speech, as if drunk
- rapid pulse, shallow breathing
- possible unconsciousness.

1. Examine the casualty for a card or bracelet indicating that he or she is diabetic.
2. If the casualty is conscious, raise blood sugar levels immediately by giving sugar lumps, sweet drinks, chocolate, jam, honey or other sweet items.
3. If the casualty is unconscious but breathing normally, place in the recovery position (see unit 52) and summon medical help immediately. Do not give any food or drink because it may cause choking.

Poisoning

A poison is a substance which when taken into the body in sufficient quantities causes illness and even death. Poisons can be taken into the body by:

- swallowing—drug overdoses, poisonous fruits or berries, chemicals or household products. Swallowed poisons may be corrosive or non-corrosive (see box)
- inhaling—industrial or household gases—however North Sea gas is not poisonous—chemical vapours, fumes produced by faulty burners or cookers without sufficient ventilation
- injecting or absorbing—animal or insect bites, pesticides or insecticides which can be absorbed through the skin, injections by hyperdermic needles.

The circumstances in which the casualty is found may give a clue to the type of poisoning, for example an opened bottle near the casualty.

Corrosive poisons cause burning and white discolouration on the mouth, lips and clothes, intense pain in the stomach, gut, mouth or lips. Other poisons act in different ways. Some affect the breathing, others the central nervous system, the heart or the blood. Some result in retching, vomiting or diarrhoea.

As some poisons will quickly cause unconsciousness, it is important to ask the casualty as soon as possible what has been taken, how much and how long ago. Look around and note any evidence of the type of poison involved. The doctors will find this information and any samples that can be sent with the casualty helpful.

Whether the casualty is conscious or not, move him or her into the recovery position, providing breathing is satisfactory (see unit 52), and call for an ambulance.

For corrosive poisoning, give small sips of milk or water to dilute the poison, gently flush out the mouth and sponge away traces of poison, remove poison-soaked clothing.

Do not induce vomiting whatever poison has been taken. Vomiting will not do any good and could even make the situation worse.

Check breathing and heartbeat regularly and if necessary resuscitate (see units 54 and 55). If the casualty's mouth has been burnt by the poison, blow air into his or her lungs through the nose.

Some poisons

Corrosive	Non-corrosive
ammonia	alcohol
bleach	aspirin
caustic soda	berries
detergents	medicines
disinfectants	methylated
floor and furniture	spirits
polish	mushrooms
lighter fuel	and fungi
nail varnish	seeds
paraffin	sleeping pills
petrol	snail bait
shampoo	
turpentine	
washing powder	

Air contains about 20% oxygen. When air is breathed in, the body absorbs some of this oxygen into the bloodstream. The air which is expelled as a person breathes out contains only slightly less oxygen (about 16%) and a small amount of carbon dioxide. The retained oxygen is vital to life. The technique of mouth-to-mouth resuscitation uses the oxygen which is expelled from the first aider's lungs to provide the casualty's body with its own vital supply of oxygen until he or she can breathe again.

Providing help to an unconscious casualty

The first step is to check if the casualty is breathing:

- Put your ear to the casualty's mouth to feel and hear the breathing.
- Watch the chest and put your hand on it to check its rise and fall.
- Look at the colour of the casualty's lips, cheeks and ear lobes. They are likely to have gone blue-grey if breathing has stopped.

If the casualty is not breathing:

1. Open and clear the airway (see HOW TO box).
2. Give mouth-to-mouth resuscitation (see HOW TO box). Give resuscitation even if you do not think the casualty can be revived.
3. Continue giving resuscitation until breathing and heartbeat have returned, or until medical help has arrived, or until you are too exhausted to continue. (Dealing with a casualty whose heart has stopped beating is covered in the next unit.)
4. Once breathing has returned, the casualty should be put into the recovery position (see HOW TO box in unit 52).
5. Observe the casualty carefully and be prepared to restart resuscitation if breathing stops.

What can stop people breathing

Head injuries
Electric shock
Inhaling gas or other fumes
Poisoning
Obstructed airway

✱ FOR INTEREST

The average rate of breathing for an adult is 15 to 18 breaths a minute. In babies and young children the rate is 20 to 40 breaths a minute. The rate increases if more oxygen is required, for example when taking exercise or when in distress.

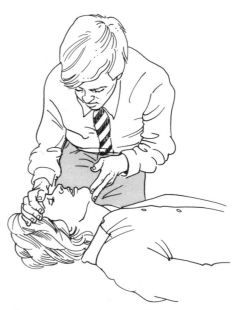

The open airway position: chin up, forehead down. Once the airway is open, the casualty might begin breathing spontaneously. The casualty should then be placed in the recovery position

---

?? HOW TO

Open and clear the airway

1. Lie the casualty on his or her back.
2. Tilt the head back. To do this press one hand gently on the forehead and the other hand under the neck, lifting gently. Then keeping one hand pressing down on the forehead place the fingers or palm of the other hand under the chin and lift it. If the tongue has fallen back, this will bring it forward, clear of the airway.
3. If breathing does not start normally, or if the breathing is noisy, the airway may be blocked. To clear it:
   – turn the casualty's head to one side
   – feel gently inside the mouth with the fingers (the first two fingers are usually the best to use) and remove vomit, dentures and any other foreign bodies from the mouth
   – but be careful not to push any obstacles further down the throat.

‼ REMEMBER

Do not use the first aid technique of mouth-to-mouth resuscitation until you have received proper training from a qualified instructor.

▶ ▶ ▶ TO DO

Write down the steps you should take when you find someone lying unconscious and not breathing beside an electrical appliance. Show your work to a qualified first aider and ask him or her to help you clarify any points you have not covered properly. Then revise your steps.

??   **HOW TO**

Give mouth-to-mouth resuscitation

1. Place the casualty on his or her back. Remove any obstructions around the face or neck and loosen tight clothing. It is easiest to carry out mouth-to-mouth resuscitation if the casualty is lying on his or her back. But it is important to start the treatment very quickly, so do not waste valuable time trying to move the patient into the ideal position.
2. Open the airway and remove any obstacles. It is very important to give the first two inflations as quickly as possible so do not waste time looking for hidden obstacles.
3. Take in a deep breath through your mouth.
4. Pinch the casualty's nose shut. Open the casualty's mouth and seal your lips around it.
5. Breathe firmly into the casualty's mouth and slowly empty your lungs. Watch the casualty's chest as you blow the air in, so you can see it expand and rise slightly. Do not blow too hard or too fast. A gentle, but firm and rhythmic movement is more likely to be effective.

6. If the casualty's chest fails to rise as you blow the air in, assume the airway is not open and repeat step 2. If there is still no sign of movement the airway must be obstructed and you will have to treat the casualty for choking (see unit 51).
7. Take your mouth away and take another deep breath. As you do this watch the casualty's chest to check that it falls and there is no blockage.
8. After you have ventilated the casualty's lungs twice in this way, check that the heart is beating (see unit 55). If it is not beating, there is no point in continuing resuscitation because the oxygen will not be able to circulate around the body. The treatment will have to be changed to get the heart beating (see unit 55).
9. If the heart is beating, continue to give 12 to 16 inflations per minute until the casualty is breathing without help. Mouth-to-mouth resuscitation can be very tiring. If possible take it in turns with someone else.
10. If the casualty vomits, turn the head to one side, clear out the mouth and resume resuscitation.
11. When the casualty is breathing without help, place him or her in the recovery position (see unit 52).
12. Keep a check on breathing and pulse rate until medical help arrives.

Children and babies
- Place your mouth over the child's mouth and seal your lips as in step 4. For babies under the age of two, seal your mouth over the mouth and nose.
- Blow very gently and use shallow breaths. Remember a child's lungs are much smaller than an adult's.
- Continue to give inflations at 20 per minute (step 9).

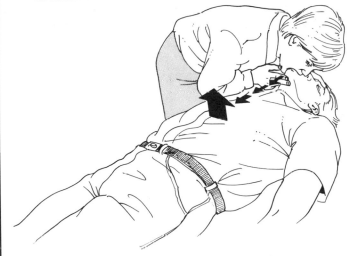

As you breathe into the casualty's mouth, keep an eye on the chest movement

---

✱ FOR INTEREST

Mouth-to-mouth resuscitation is regarded by first aid experts as the preferred method of treatment when a casualty is not breathing. If the mouth cannot be used, for instance because it is burnt, then resuscitation can be given through the nose. In this case hold the casualty's mouth shut and seal your lips around the nose.

Mouth-to-mouth resuscitation should never be withheld in an emergency through fear of catching AIDS (see unit 45). No case of infection has been reported from any part of the world as a result of giving mouth-to-mouth resuscitation.

If the casualty's heart has stopped beating and there is no pulse, blood containing oxygen does not circulate around the body. Permanent damage to the brain will occur if it is deprived of oxygen for more than three minutes. After six minutes the casualty will die.

The action of the heart causes a pulsing movement in the blood vessels which carry the blood away from the heart—the arteries. Where an artery is close to the surface this movement can be felt, particularly when the artery can be squeezed against a bone, as at the wrist, or against a muscle, as at the neck.

Providing help to a casualty whose heart has stopped

It is important to be quite sure that the casualty's heart has stopped before giving external chest compression (as the treatment is known). The heart action is delicate and unnecessary treatment will almost certainly upset it, possibly stopping a heart which was functioning rather weakly.

1. If the casualty is not breathing give mouth-to-mouth resuscitation (see unit 54).
2. After giving two inflations, check the casualty's pulse (see HOW TO box).
3. If there is no pulse, give external chest compression alternating with mouth-to-mouth resuscitation (see HOW TO box).
4. When the heart is beating, and if the patient is still not breathing, continue with mouth-to-mouth resuscitation.
5. If another first-aider is available to help you, one person can give mouth-to-mouth resuscitation while the other gives external chest compression.
6. When breathing has resumed, put the casualty in the recovery position (see unit 52).

➤ ➤ ➤ TO DO

Practise taking the pulse of a friend, at the carotid and at the wrist. Be careful not to press too strongly. Learn to count pulse rates accurately, using a watch with a second hand.

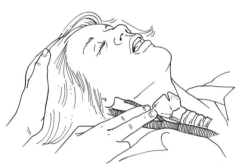

Checking the carotid pulse

?? HOW TO

Check the heart beat

1. Note the casualty's appearance: blue-grey lips, cheeks and ear lobes, and/or dilated pupils can indicate no heartbeat.
2. Put your ear to the left side of the breast bone to hear if the heart is beating.
3. Gently press a pulse point with two or three fingers (not your thumb as it has its own pulse):
   – to take the carotid pulse, place your fingers on the side of the casualty's neck, near the voice box and slide them down into the hollow between the voice box and the muscle near it
   – to take the radial pulse, press the tips of your fingers lightly into the wrist (on the same side as the palm of the casualty's hand), in line with the base of the thumb.
   Note: the radial pulse is unreliable when the heart is beating weakly.
4. Count the number of beats in 30 seconds and multiply by two to give the number of beats per minute. The normal pulse rate for adults is 60 to 80 beats a minute. It increases during stress, when taking exercise or drinking alcohol, or as a result of injury (or certain illnesses). In babies and children the normal rate is 90 to 140 beats a minute.
5. Check the pulse after one minute and then at three minute intervals until medical help arrives.

Checking the radial pulse

??   HOW TO

Give external chest compression

1. Lay the casualty on the back on a firm, flat surface, with the head also lying flat, facing directly upwards.
2. Kneel on one side of the casualty, at the level of the chest and in line with the heart.
3. Find the junction of the rib bones at the bottom of the casualty's breast-bone. Place the heel of one hand along the line of the breast-bone, about two fingers breadth up from the junction point. Only the heel of the hand should be used to exert pressure, so keep the fingers up.

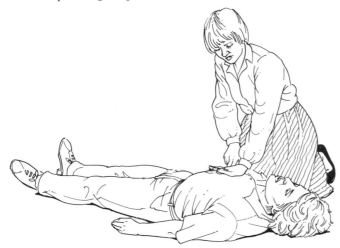

4. Place the heel of the other hand on the back of the first hand, and lock the fingers together.

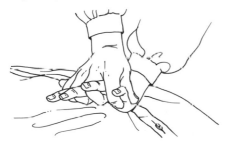

5. Keeping the arms straight, move forward continuing to press down until your arms are vertical over your hands. This will move the breast-bone of an average adult 4 to 5 cm (1½ to 2 inches).
6. Move your body backwards to relieve the pressure, but leave your hands in position on the breast-bone.
7. Rock gently and steadily backwards and forwards, so allowing your body weight to do the work. Do this 15 times at the rate of:
   – 80 times a minute for adults
   – 100 times a minute for children, using one hand only and causing the breast-bone to move between 2.5 and 3.5 cm (1 to 1½ inches)
   – 100 times a minute for babies and children under two years of age, using two fingers only and causing the breast-bone to move between 1.5 and 2.5 cm (½ to 1 inch).

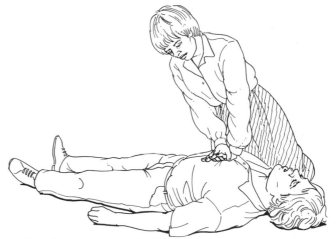

8. Move the casualty's head to the side and re-open the airway (see unit 54).
9. Give two inflations of mouth-to-mouth resuscitation (see unit 54).
10. Continue with the cycle of external chest compression and mouth-to-mouth resuscitation.
11. Check the carotid pulse regularly. It is important to stop giving external chest compression as soon as the heart has started beating (to continue may cause it to fail again).

!!   REMEMBER

Do not use the first aid technique of external chest compression until you have received training from a qualified instructor.

Bleeding is loss of blood from the circulatory system, a network of arteries, veins and capillaries which carry the blood round the body.

- The commonest type of bleeding is when the blood oozes out from a shallow cut or wound. It indicates that the smallest blood vessels, the capillaries, are damaged.
- If the injury has damaged a vein, dark red blood will gush out. Severe bleeding must be controlled immediately.
- The most serious type of bleeding is from the arteries. The blood is bright red and frequently spurts out from the wound in a pump-like action in time with the heart beat.

Bleeding can be controlled by slowing down the flow of blood to the wound. This allows blood clots to form and plug up the damaged vessels. The more slowly the blood flows the easier it is for clots to form.

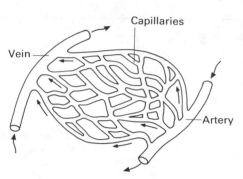

The strongest of the blood vessels, the arteries, carry blood away from the heart. As they move out into the body the arteries divide and become smaller until they become capillaries. In effect a thin layer of cells, the capillaries enable the exchange of fluids and gases to and from the tissue cells of the body. Having done this, the capillaries join up to become veins and return the blood to the heart

External bleeding

Usually the bleeding is clearly visible. However, after an accident, particularly in the dark, the casualty's position may conceal a serious wound.

Look for other warning signs and very gently, without moving the casualty, feel over and under the body for patches of sticky dampness. Assume they are blood until there is evidence they are not.

Internal bleeding

This occurs when blood escapes from the circulatory system, but remains in the body. Internal bleeding may be visible, as when a casualty coughs up or vomits blood after injuries to the chest or digestive system, or invisible when it may be inside one of the body cavities or in the form of a bruise as a result of a bone fracture.

It is difficult to gauge the extent of the injury with internal bleeding and so it is important to treat all cases as very serious and call for urgent medical help. In the meantime:

- try and calm the casualty, keep him or her warm and as comfortable as possible
- help maintain the supply of blood to the brain, so if possible lie the casualty down with feet raised slightly and head to one side and loosen any tight clothing around the neck, chest or waist
- check breathing and pulse rates at ten minute intervals and keep a record for the doctors
- keep a record also of any specimen passed by the casualty or vomited, and if possible a sample which can be sent to the hospital when help arrives
- provide mouth-to-mouth resuscitation and external chest compression if necessary (see units 54 and 55)
- if the casualty becomes conscious, open the airway and place in the recovery position (see units 52 and 54).

Signs of bleeding

General
Pale skin, clammy and cold
Heavy sweating
Fast, but weak pulse
Thirst
Anxiety, restlessness
Blurring of vision
Giddiness, faintness or in some cases unconsciousness

External bleeding
Escaping blood

Internal bleeding
Vomiting frothy, bright red blood
Swelling
Fingers and toes blue and cold

 **TO DO**

Describe to a qualified first-aider what action should be taken if someone is bleeding heavily from a deep cut on the arm. Ask the first-aider to show you the dressings available to treat such a wound and explain how each is used (see also unit 60).

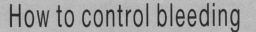

✱ FOR INTEREST

Adults have 5 litres (9 pints) of blood in their body depending on the size of the person.

Normally an adult can lose 850 ml (1½ pints) blood without a serious problem, but the loss of 1.7 litres (3 pints) can be critical.

Blood loss can look more serious than it is with cuts and external bleeding, especially with nose-bleeds. But watery-looking blood-stained fluid running from the nose may be a sign of a fractured skull.

Severe bruising, especially when associated with a limb fracture which may have perforated a blood vessel, can cause heavy internal bleeding.

Mild bleeding stops of its own accord as the blood clots. The application of firm pressure over the bleeding point will encourage this.

There is a pressure point on each arm and each side of the groin which can be used to control severe bleeding by preventing the flow of blood through important arteries. But this method should only be used by experts and then as a last resort.

Grazes generally result from a sliding fall, and there is usually very little bleeding from the raw area.
Clean cuts—known as *incised wounds*—are frequently caused by a sharp instrument like a razor blade, knife or glass. Bleeding may be profuse.
Torn or *lacerated* wounds are rough-edged and jagged. They are likely to be caused by barbed wire or other rough-edged object. They are very likely to be contaminated by dirt and bacteria.
Puncture wounds are the deep, small wounds caused by needles, nails or other sharp items. Dirt and bacteria may be taken into the wound and infection is common.

?? HOW TO

Control a nose-bleed

1. Sit the casualty with head well forward, at a table if possible.
2. Loosen tight clothing around neck and chest.
3. Place a bowl in the casualty's hands or on the table.
4. Tell the casualty to breathe through the mouth and pinch the soft part of the nose tightly for at least 10 minutes.
5. Encourage the casualty to let the blood dribble into the bowl and avoid swallowing blood (to avoid nausea and vomiting) or coughing, sniffing or spitting.
6. After 10 minutes release pressure. If nose is still bleeding, continue for up to 30 minutes.
7. When the bleeding has stopped and while the casualty's head is still forward, provide a swab or clean dressing soaked in luke-warm water so the casualty can clean around the nose and mouth. Do not plug the nose.
8. If after 30 minutes the bleeding has not stopped, call for medical help.

?? HOW TO

Treat grazes, cuts and wounds

1. If possible wash your hands before dealing with the wound.
2. Examine the wound and carefully wipe or wash off any small foreign bodies. Use a swab or rinse under cold running water. Large foreign bodies should be left where they are. They may be plugging the wound and any attempt to remove them could cause further injury.
3. If the wound is minor:
   – clean it if it is dirty (under running water or with a swab)
   – clean the surrounding area
   – gently dry the wound and surrounding area with clean swabs
   – if the wound is still bleeding press a swab or dressing against it, and raise the injured part to slow the flow of blood
   – cover the wound with a suitable dressing (see unit 60)
   – if the wound is more than 1.75 cm (½ inch) in length it may need stitching in hospital
   – if the wound is likely to have been contaminated by dirt or bacteria, the casualty must be taken to hospital for treatment against tetanus
4. If there is major external bleeding:
   – place a suitable absorbent dressing over the wound and hold it in place firmly (the dressing should be large enough to extend beyond the area of the wound)
   – if a dressing is not immediately available use your bare hands
   – if the wound is gaping squeeze the edges together
   – raise the wounded part of the body (unless it is a fracture, see unit 59)
   – place over the dressing a bandage, tying it firmly enough to control the bleeding but not so tight it restricts circulation
   – if the bleeding continues do not remove the dressing, but place further dressings over the top and bandage firmly
   – treat for shock if necessary (see unit 57)
   – call for urgent medical help.
5. If a foreign body has to be left in the wound, dress the wound carefully so that the object is not likely to be caught or moved further into the body.
6. If a part of the casualty's body such as a finger or toe has been cut off in the accident:
   – take special care not to damage the stump
   – place the severed part in a clean container such as a plastic bag to prevent it drying out or becoming contaminated
   – if possible keep the bag (sealed) in another container of ice
   – label the package with the casualty's name and the time of the accident.

‼ REMEMBER

Blood can carry harmful viruses such as the HIV virus which causes AIDS. Always wash your hands before and immediately after treating wounds. Cover any exposed cuts or breaks in your own skin with a waterproof dressing (see unit 60).

Any problem to do with the circulation of blood around a person's body is serious. If the casualty is suffering from shock as the result of a serious injury, electric shock or an emotional trauma, for example, the supply of blood around the body may slow right down or even stop. A serious heart attack will certainly cause breathing and heartbeat to stop and if the person has suffered a stroke it means the supply of blood to part of the brain is critically affected. That part of the brain will stop functioning, probably permanently.

Signs and symptoms

SHOCK
Pale, cold, clammy skin
Weakness and giddiness
Sweating
Pulse fast and weak
Breathing shallow and rapid
Thirst
Nausea and vomiting
Unconsciousness

HEART ATTACK
Sudden severe pain in the chest, usually central but may radiate to the jaw, throat, arms and back
Dizziness and giddiness
Ashen face, lips may turn blue
Heavy sweating
Rapid, weak pulse, which may be irregular
Breathlessness
Shock
Unconsciousness, leading to loss of breathing and heartbeat
if the attack is severe

STROKE
Sudden severe headache
Confusion and disorientation
Pounding of the pulse
Dizziness
Weakness and numbness down one side of the body
Slurred speech or difficulty in speaking
Hot and dry skin with flushed face
May be loss of bladder or bowel control
Pupils may be unequally dilated

---

1. The priority in all cases is to restore breathing and heartbeat and to summon urgent medical help (see units 54 and 55).
2. If the casualty is still unconscious, he or she should be put in the recovery position (see unit 52).
3. Loosen any tight clothing around the neck, chest or waist.
4. Stop any bleeding (see unit 56 and HOW TO boxes in this unit).
5. If the casualty is conscious and has suffered:
   Shock, lie him or her down, with the legs raised to help return the supply of blood to the head. The head should be put to one side to reduce the risk of vomiting. If breathing becomes difficult put the casualty in the recovery position.
   Heart attack, place him or her down on the floor in a half-sitting position, leaning back at an angle (you will need to support the casualty's head and shoulders) and knees bent.
   Stroke, lie him or her down with the head and shoulders slightly raised, head to one side.
6. Otherwise help the casualty to be as comfortable as possible:
   – keep other people away
   – provide calm reassurance
   – do not move the casualty to another area unless there is imminent danger
   – if it is cold, keep the casualty warm, covering with a coat or blanket, but do not use a hot water bottle as it will draw blood to the surface of the body away from the vital organs.
7. Do not give the casualty anything to drink or eat. The lips should be moistened with water if the casualty is suffering from shock. If the casualty has only suffered from an emotional shock and you are certain there will be no need for an anaesthetic later, you can give him or her a little to drink.

▶▶▶ TO DO

An injury can cause shock if it leads to:

- severe loss of blood internally or externally
- severe loss of body fluid through the skin surface in severe burns
- severe loss of fluid through recurrent diarrhoea or vomiting
- severe bruising especially after a fracture
- any condition that briefly interrupts the steady beating of the heart.

For one of these situations describe what additional first aid action would help a casualty suffering from shock. Refer to other FIRST AID units as necessary and discuss your answer with a qualified first-aider.

?? HOW TO

Treat bleeding from the mouth

1. Sit the casualty down with head bent forward and to one side so the blood can run out one side of the mouth.
2. Place a clean dressing over the wound and apply direct pressure for 10 to 20 minutes. It is usually easier for the casualty to hold the dressing himself or herself—if seated at a table this will be more comfortable.
3. If bleeding continues after 20 minutes, change the dressing. Try and do this without disturbing the clot.
4. Summon medical help.

?? HOW TO

Treat bleeding from the ear

Bleeding from the ear following a fall or a blow to the head may mean a fractured skull. Watery fluid may also be emitted.

1. If breathing and/or heartbeat have stopped, resuscitate immediately (see units 54 and 55).
2. If the casualty is conscious, place him or her in a half-sitting, half-lying position (propped up with cushions or folded clothing), head leaning over to the injured side to allow drainage.
3. If the casualty is unconscious but breathing satisfactorily, place him or her in the recovery position (see unit 52) with head positioned so the blood and fluids from the injured ear can drain out.
4. Send for medical help.
5. Cover the ear with a sterile dressing pad, secured adequately but not tightly with a bandage or adhesive dressing. Never plug the ear to stop the flow of blood.

?? HOW TO

Treat an eye wound

All eye wounds should be considered serious. Superficial scratches may damage the cornea, affecting the vision.

1. Do not attempt to remove any foreign bodies from the eye.
2. Lie the casualty down, keeping the head still.
3. Ask the casualty to close the injured eye. If possible cover it with a sterile pad.
4. Advise the casualty to keep both eyes absolutely still. Movement may cause further injury. If necessary blindfold the casualty to protect the eyes from movement.
5. Reassure the casualty and seek medical help.

Burns and scalds are injuries to the body tissue as a result of contact with or exposure to heat, extreme cold, chemicals, radiation and electricity. They can cause severe shock due to loss of body fluids, and infection because of the damage to the skin.

- First degree or superficial burns involve only the outer layers of the skin. Obvious signs are redness, tenderness and sometimes swelling and peeling of the skin. They usually heal well.
- Second degree or intermediate burns can affect several layers of the skin leading to peeling, blisters, inflammation and swelling of the surrounding skin. Subsequent infection is common and medical advice should be sought.
- Third degree or deep burns penetrate all layers of the skin and frequently the underlying tissue, which becomes grey and charred. Though they are often less painful than superficial burns because the nerves have been damaged, severe shock may result. It is essential that these burns received immediate medical attention.

Dry burns are caused by flames, heat from electrical appliances, lighted cigarettes or friction (for example from a rope).

Scalds are produced by wet heat in the form of steam, very hot water or fat.

Electrical burns are caused by a high voltage passing through the body.

Chemical burns are caused by acids and alkalis (frequently found in cleaning agents).

Cold burns are caused by contact with metals in frozen conditions or with freezing agents such as liquid oxygen and liquid nitrogen.

Radiation burns are caused by over exposure to the sun, or, rarely, by X-rays.

---

1. Place the injured part under a running tap or pour cold (but not iced) water over for at least ten minutes or longer, until the pain is relieved. If there is no water available use a harmless cold liquid such as milk or beer. Do not apply any lotion, ointment or fat to the injury.
2. If the wound is severe:
   – lie the casualty down, but if possible protect the burnt area from the ground
   – check breathing and heartbeat and resuscitate if necessary (see units 54 and 55)
   – if the casualty is breathing but unconscious, put him or her in the recovery position (see unit 52)
   – treat for shock (see unit 57).
3. As soon as possible, gently remove any jewellery, clothing or footwear which might restrict swelling.
4. Do not break blisters or remove loose skin. Blisters will normally heal themselves. If necessary protect blisters with a dressing so they will not get damaged, resulting in an infection.
5. Dry the area and apply a clean dressing, preferably sterile (see unit 60). Do not use an adhesive dressing. A large area can be covered with a clean sheet or pillow case for example, an injured hand or food with an unused plastic bag.
6. If possible, raise the affected part of the body to reduce swelling.
7. Reassure the casualty.
8. If the burn is deeper than the skin, or covers an area greater than 2 to 3 cm (1 inch) in diameter, call for medical help.
9. If the burn is in the mouth or throat, it is obviously not possible to dress the wound. Give the casualty frequent sips of cold water and try and keep him or

her as calm as possible. The throat will swell rapidly and there is a danger of asphyxia (see unit 52). Look out for and retain any bottles or containers of possible corrosive fluid that might have caused the burn. Pass these to the professionals when they arrive.

10. If the burn is caused by a chemical, for instance a strong cleaning agent, paint stripper or acid:
    – douse the burnt area continuously for at least ten minutes with cold water from a tap or jug
    – carefully remove all contaminated clothing during dousing, avoiding contact with the chemical
    – if the eyes have been burnt, treat the eyes first by rinsing them under gently running water for at least ten minutes. Make sure the water does not run into the casualty's mouth or, if only one eye has been injured, into the good eye. Do not allow the casualty to rub his or her eye.

▶ ▶ ▶ TO DO

Think carefully about the sort of burns and scalds that might occur in a work situation of your choice, for instance in a catering kitchen, the bar or cellar area, housekeeping or maintenance. Talk to some people who have had experience of dealing with burns and scalds, including if possible a first-aider in charge of your chosen work situation. Decide what the two main dangers are and draw up a checklist to help prevent those types of accident.

‼ REMEMBER

- If the cause is electrical, switch off the power source or pull out the plug, taking care not to electrocute yourself, before touching the casualty.
- The greater the area of a burn the more likely the casualty is to suffer shock (see unit 57). This is because fluids leak out of the body's circulatory system into the burnt area.
- In the early stages it is often difficult to tell what sort of burn the casualty has suffered. A large burn will probably contain all three types. If in any doubt about the seriousness of a burn, or if the casualty is elderly, sick or very young, always call medical help.
- If the casualty's clothing is on fire, douse the flames with water or wrap a thick blanket, preferably a fire blanket, or curtain tightly around the casualty.

- Do not roll the casualty along the ground as this can spread the burning. Never use any synthetic material that will melt.
- If the casualty's clothing has been soaked in the burning liquid, remove the clothing as soon as it has cooled sufficiently, if necessary by carefully cutting it away. On the other hand if the clothing has burnt dry, do not attempt to remove it. The heat will have sterilised it. Never attempt to remove anything which is sticking to the burn.
- Be careful not to infect burnt areas, for instance by breathing over them or touching them.
- Never give anyone who is unconscious, or is likely to need an anaesthetic, anything to drink.

A fracture is a break, crack or split in a bone. Usually a fairly strong force is necessary to break a bone, but as people grow older their bones become more brittle with the result that they break more easily and take longer to heal.

A fracture may be suspected because the casualty has fallen, or suffered a blow. Perhaps he or she claims to have heard a bone snap or feel it break, or feels severe pain at or near to the site of the injury, which increases when the injured part is moved. The casualty may be in a state of shock. There may be tenderness around the injury and/or swelling and bruising.

The fracture may be quite obvious with deformity, shortening, twisting or injured limb or bone protruding through the skin.

The fracture may be closed, where the broken bone does not penetrate through the skin, or open, where the bone breaks the skin and can sometimes be seen protruding through. Both types of fracture can be complicated by injury to surrounding muscles, blood vessels, nerves or adjacent organs. Bleeding will be evident with an open fracture. Internal bleeding is likely to follow a closed fracture.

Comminuted fractures occur when the bone is crushed and shattered into pieces. With children, the bone may not be completely broken, but split on one side and buckled at the other. Children's bones are not yet fully hardened. This type of break heals quickly.

‼ REMEMBER

- If you suspect the casualty has a neck or spine fracture do not attempt to move him or her. Special procedures have to be followed to avoid causing very serious damage to the body's nerve system.
- If you are in any doubt about the nature of the injury treat as a fracture.
- Do not touch the bone or immediate surrounding area.
- Never force an injured limb into a particular position to immobilise it.
- If the ambulance will be arriving very quickly do not attempt to bandage the casualty, but support the injured area until medical help arrives.

---

1. Check breathing and heartbeat and resuscitate if necessary (see units 54 and 55). Treat for shock if necessary (see unit 57).
2. Summon medical help.
3. Do not move the casualty unless his or her life is in danger, for example because the building is collapsing. If movement is unavoidable, try not to increase pain. If possible immobilise and support the limb before moving.
4. If the fracture is open, cover the damaged flesh with a clean dressing. Apply pressure around the wound to control bleeding. If the bone is protruding put a ring pad around it and build up with extra padding to prevent pressure. Bandage firmly.
5. Protect the casualty from the cold and keep him or her as comfortable and calm as possible.
6. Immobilise the injury and where possible raise the injured part to prevent swelling. In many cases another part of the casualty's body will provide adequate support, for example bandaging an injured leg to the other, good, leg. Any sharp points such as the knee and any hollows, for example under the arm, may need to be padded. With a limb injury it is essential to immobilise the joints above and below the fracture. Bandages should not be tied so firmly as to interfere with the circulation.

Arm fractures
- Sit the casualty down.
- Gently support the limb across the front of the chest, with the forearm lying in a horizontal position or pointing up at a slight angle.
- Place soft padding between the arm and the chest and support with an arm sling.
- If possible, secure the supported arm on to the chest with another bandage.

Collar-bone fractures
- Place the arm on the affected side over the front of the chest with the fingertips on the opposite shoulder.
- Place padding between the arm and the chest.
- Support the arm and padding in a sling.
- Tie the sling to the chest with a broad bandage.

Lower leg fractures
- Lie the casualty down, carefully support the injured limb.
- Holding the casualty's ankle and foot, carefully pull away from the body in a straight line so as to straighten the leg.
- Place padding under the casualty's knees and above and below the fracture.
- Gently move the injured limb until it is lying alongside the other limb. Maintain the gentle pulling movement from the foot.
- Tie a figure-of-eight bandage around the ankles and other bandages above the casualty's knees and above and below the fracture on the lower leg.

Two people are required to bring an injured leg into its normal straight line

---

 TO DO

With the help of a qualified first-aider and a friend, practise bandaging a supposed fracture in the forearm of your friend.

Avoid jerky movements when bandaging an injured limb. Tie the knots away from the injury. Do not bandage directly over the fractured area. So if the injury was near the ankle, as in this illustration, the bandage would have to be much closer to or over the feet

Dressings

Dressings are the best type of covering for wounds. They provide a soft, protective pad:

- preventing dirt or bacteria from entering the wound
- absorbing blood and fluids produced by the wound
- allowing sweat released by the skin to evaporate
- helping the blood to clot. Even though a dressing often sticks to the wound and can be quite painful to remove, the benefits are greater than any disadvantage.

Small wounds are often covered with an adhesive dressing (a plaster). These have an area of absorbent gauze attached to an adhesive backing. Waterproof backings are best—and they are the only type that can be used by someone who handles food (see unit 17). But waterproof dressings should not be left on for more than a few hours, otherwise the skin around the wound gets very moist and the dressing sodden. This will encourage the growth of bacteria.

Sterile dressings consist of an area of fine gauze or lint (which is placed over the wound), covered by cotton wool padding. This is attached to a roll of bandage and the bandage is secured with a reef knot. Sterile dressings come in a variety of sizes and they are suitable for most wounds. First-aiders prefer them to adhesive-backed dressings or any other combination of dressing and bandage.

Gauze dressings are suitable for large wounds or burns. They have to be covered with a pad of cotton wool and held in place with adhesive strapping or a bandage.

> **‼ REMEMBER**
> - Place a dressing directly on to the wound. Do not slide it over from one side.
> - Never use a sterile dressing (the combined dressing and bandage) if the seal of its protective wrapping has been damaged.
> - When using an adhesive dressing always make sure the area around the wound is dry. If there is any moisture the plaster will fall off.
> - If a dressing quickly becomes stained by blood, cover it with another dressing and re-bandage more firmly.
> - Wash your hands before and after attending to a wound.
> - Never talk or cough over a wound or dressing.
> - Do not touch the wound or any part of the dressing which will come into contact with the wound.
> - If the dressing falls out of position before it can be bandaged, throw it away and start again with a new dressing. The first one may have become contaminated.
> - Adhesive bandages cause a skin reaction on some people. Check before using one.

Bandages

The two types of bandage most widely used are the triangular bandage and the roller bandage. They will:

- hold a dressing in place and, if required, apply pressure over the wound to control bleeding
- support an injured part of the body and, if required, help stop it moving
- reduce or, in some cases, prevent swelling
- help absorb blood and fluids produced by the wound.

Bandages are usually made of cotton, calico, elastic net or special paper. Ordinary bandages are not particularly soft (the combined dressing and bandage type is the exception). They should be used with a dressing for any wound.

> **‼ REMEMBER**
> - When dressings or bandages are not available, clean sheets, towels, pillow cases and handkerchiefs can be cut or torn to form bandages. But never place cotton wool or any fluffy material directly on to a wound. The fibres will get caught up in the wound.
> - Slings can be made from scarves or ties, and the arms of coats or jumpers can be pinned to support wrists or arms.
> - However if accidents happen in the workplace, sufficient dressings and bandages must, by law, be available (see unit 13).

There are some general rules for applying bandages. The casualty should be as relaxed as possible, preferably sitting or lying down. If the bandage is to remain firm, it is important that the injured part is bandaged in a position which will help recovery and not be unnecessarily uncomfortable or awkward. The first-aider should choose a convenient position to work from, for instance standing in front of a seated casualty, by the injured side.

The bandages should hold the dressing firmly in position, and if necessary apply enough pressure to control bleeding or prevent movement. But if the bandage is too tight it will slow down or stop the circulation of blood to parts of the casualty's body. To prevent this happening check every ten minutes or so for:

- any swelling of the injured part
- any visible signs of poor circulation. For example if the arm is bandaged and the casualty complains of tingling or lack of feeling in the fingers, or the fingers go very cold, or the finger nails go pale or blue, or there is loss of movement in the casualty's fingers. If the leg is bandaged the toes provide a visible means of checking the circulation. If a finger or toe nail or any exposed skin at the extremity of the injured limb is pressed with a finger until it goes white, once the pressure is released the colour should return quickly.

- a weakening of the radial pulse, if the injury is on an arm (see unit 55). There is a pulse point at the ankle joint of the leg, but considerable experience is needed to locate it and take the pulse accurately.

The bandage should be loosened slightly as soon as there is any sign of it interfering with the circulation.

The knot of the bandage can be positioned over the injury to help apply pressure if this is important. But if the purpose of the bandage is to prevent movement, and a knot would increase the pain felt by the casualty it should be positioned well away from the injured part.

If, for example, an arm is being bandaged against the chest, then it may be necessary to use padding to help protect the arm from uncomfortably sharp rib bones.

Triangular bandages

These usually have sides one metre (39 inches) in length. They are the ideal shape for making a sling to support or provide protection for the arm or chest. They are also big enough to secure dressings over areas such as the head, hand or foot, and if folded (see HOW TO box) will help immobilise limbs or secure dressings.

Roller bandages

Roller bandages are usually made of gauze or linen and come in 5 metre (5½ yards) strips of varying widths, for example:

2.5 cm (1 inch) wide for fingers
5 or 6 cm (2 or 2½ inches) wide for hands and arms
7.5 or 9 cm (3 or 3½ inches) wide for legs
10 or 15 cm (4 or 6 inches) wide for the chest.

 TO DO

Take a piece of bandage, ribbon or string and practise tying a reef knot. If you already can tie reef knots, or have quickly become an expert, find a friend who doesn't yet have the skill and teach her or him how to tie this type of knot.

?? **HOW TO**

Fold a triangular bandage

if it is being used to immobilise a limb or to hold a dressing.

1. Lay the bandage out on a clean, flat surface. Fold the point down to the base.

2. Fold the bandage in half again in the same direction.
3. If a narrower bandage is required fold over once more.

?? **HOW TO**

Tie a reef knot

Always secure the ends of a bandage with a reef knot because it will not slip, is easy to untie and lies flat, making it more comfortable for the casualty. Once tied the ends can be tucked neatly out of sight so they do not get caught on anything.

1. Take hold of both ends of the bandage, one end in each hand. Hold the bandage about 70 cm (3 inches) away from the ends.
2. Put the left end over the right and then under it.
3. Bring both ends together again. This time put the right end over the left and then under it.
4. Pull the two ends gently but firmly to tighten the knot.

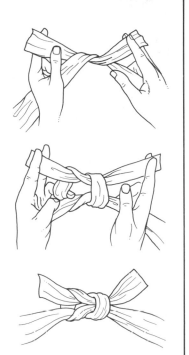

?? **HOW TO**

Secure a roller bandage

1. Fold in the end of the bandage and secure with a safety pin, adhesive tape or a special bandage clip.
2. Alternatively leave about 15 cm (6 inches) of the bandage free, but more if you are bandaging a thick part of the body.

   - Cut down through the centre of this to split the loose bandage into two.
   - Tie a reef knot where the split starts (to prevent the bandage splitting any further).
   - Take the two halves of the bandage around the body, then tie them together with a reef knot.

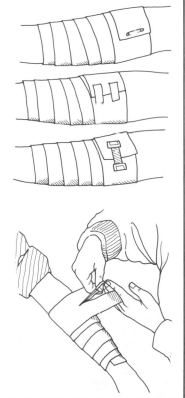

INDEX

INDEX